PRACTI
CON

Other Titles of Interest

PRACTICAL ELECTRONIC CONTROL PROJECTS

by

OWEN BISHOP

BERNARD BABANI (publishing) LTD
THE GRAMPIANS
SHEPHERDS BUSH ROAD
LONDON W6 7NF
ENGLAND

© 1996 BERNARD BABANI (publishing) LTD

First Published – July 1996

British Library Cataloguing in Publication Data

A catalogue record for this book is available from the British Library

ISBN 0 85934 377 4

Cover Design by Gregor Arthur

Printed and bound in Great Britain by Cox & Wyman Ltd, Reading

Contents

WARNING

Certain circuits and projects included in this book involve mains voltages and wiring. These are not recommended for beginners or those with little knowledge or experience of working with mains wiring and voltages.

Before attempting to build any circuits or projects that involve mains voltages or wiring, read the AC MAINS PRECAUTIONS on pages 38–40.

Chapter 1

INTRODUCTION TO CONTROL SYSTEMS

An engineer has an electric heater to keep the workshop warm. The room feels cold so the engineer switches on the heater and settles down to work. This is the most elementary form of control of workshop heating and illustrates the simplest form of control system. In this example, the system being controlled includes a switch, a heater, the workshop and its contents (including the engineer). Figure 1.1 is a diagram of the system. The system is controlled manually by opening or closing a mechanical switch.

A control system such as this has one big advantage – it is extremely simple. It has the disadvantage that it is not precise. It can not easily be used to keep the temperature to a fixed level, for example 25°C. The second disadvantage is that is does not control temperature absolutely. There are factors affecting temperature that are beyond the control of the system. For example, the heater may not be powerful enough to keep the room warm on a cold day. Other factors may affect the temperature, for example, someone may leave the door open, making the room too cold, or the engineer may light a blow-torch, making the room too hot. These disturbing factors are outside the control of the system.

If the engineer simply switches on the heater and thinks no more about it, the room may remain too cold in some circumstances or, it may become too hot in others. This illustrates another concept in control systems, that there is some desired state for the workshop temperature. A system in which the heater is turned on and then left on without any attempt to check that it reaches the desired state is known as an open loop system.

An open-loop control system can be perfectly adequate if there are no disturbing factors affecting the system. For example, the tuning control of a radio set determines which frequency the set is tuned to. It may be tuned to pick up one particular station and left at that frequency for months or years, or at least until the user want to listen to a different station. The

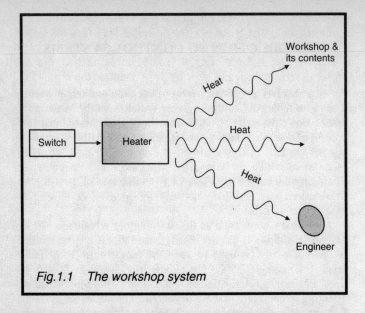

Fig.1.1   The workshop system

idling speed on a car engine may be fixed once and for all by adjusting the fuel flow to the carburettor.   It is when external changes occur, such as engine vibration altering the setting of the fuel valve, that the open loop fails to provide adequate control.

Project 1 – Demonstrating open-loop control

This project for controlling the speed of an electric motor is intended simply to demonstrate the principles of open-loop control.   It is a basic circuit so it does not give complete control. Later it is modified to improve its action. The project is not intended as a practical control circuit so you will probably prefer to set it up temporarily on a breadboard or assemble the circuit from ready-made circuit modules.

The motor suggested for this demonstration is an inexpensive d.c. motor that is rated to run at a low voltage such as 6V or 12V.   These are sold for model-makers or it is possible to

2

use a motor taken from a toy, such as a toy car. The easiest way of controlling the speed of a motor of this kind is to use a variable resistor in series with the motor to vary the voltage applied to it. There is a difficulty with this simple method. For any given voltage, the speed depends very much on the mechanical load placed on the motor; if the load is increased, the motor slows down or even stops. The outcome is worse when we try to run the motor at low speed by reducing the voltage across it; its speed is very irregular owing to the uneven frictional forces in an inexpensive motor, and the motor stalls with any slight increase in load.

The circuit shown in Figure 1.2 controls speed in a different way. The 7555 integrated circuit is running as a pulse generator. Its output (at pin 3) goes alternately high (+6V) and low (0V) several times per second. The amount of current that the 7555 can supply is not enough to drive a motor, so we use it to switch a power transistor Q1 on and off. When the output of the 7555 is high, current flows to the base of the power transistor and turns it on. When the transistor is switched on, the voltage

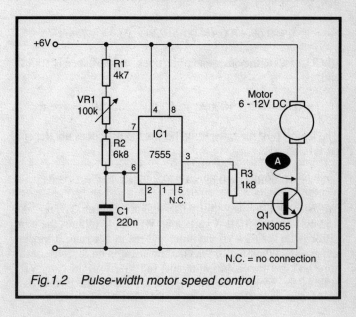

Fig.1.2   Pulse-width motor speed control

at point A drops down almost to 0V. In other words, there is almost 6V across the motor, giving a strong boost to its speed. When the output of the 7555 goes low, the transistor is switched off. The voltage at point A rises to 6V and there is no voltage across the motor. It slows down but does not stop for, almost immediately, the transistor is switched on again. In this way the circuit delivers a rapid succession of pulses to the motor to keep it running. With the component values given in Figure 1.2, the pulses are delivered 50 or more times per second, which is fast enough to appear to drive the motor at a constant speed.

The circuit has a variable resistor VR1 the effect of which is to control the length of time the output is high. The length t_1 of a high pulse is given by:

$$t_1 = 0.69(R_1 + R_2)C_1$$

where R_1 includes the resistance of R1 and that of the VR1. If VR1 is set to one end of its track so that its resistance is zero, then $R_1 = 4.7k\Omega$ and:

$$t_1 = 0.69(4700 + 6800) \times 220 \times 10^{-9} = 1.75ms$$

If VR1 is set to the other end of its track, its resistance is $100k\Omega$ and:

$$t_1 = 0.69(4700 + 100000 + 6800) \times 220 \times 10^{-9} = 16.9ms$$

The length t_2 of the low period between pulses does not depend on R1 and VR1:

$$t_2 = 0.69R_2C = 0.69 \times 6800 \times 220 \times 10^{-9} = 1.03ms$$

We use VR1 to vary the pulse length between 1.75ms and 16.9ms, a nearly 10 to 1 variation. When $t_1 = 1.75ms$, the transistor is on for 63% of the time, and the motor runs at moderate speed. When $t_1 = 16.9ms$ the transistor is on for 94% of the time and the motor runs at almost full speed. In this way VR1 acts as the speed control. Figure 1.3 shows the circuit as a block diagram. Compare this with Figure 1.1.

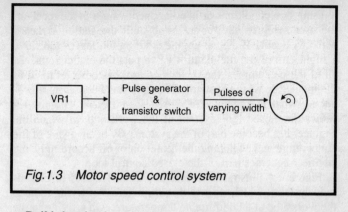

Fig.1.3   Motor speed control system

Build the circuit and experiment with it. Different motors vary in the resistance of their coils, the strength of their magnets and the friction of their bearings, so you may need to alter the values of R1, R2 or R3 to obtain exactly the same action as described below. But the suggested values are a good starting-point. Switch on the power. If the motor does not start, try turning the spindle slightly. Once the motor is running, you can vary its speed by adjusting VR1. If you have an oscilloscope, connect it to the output of the 7555 at pin 3. Notice how the speed increases as the pulse length increases.   When you have investigated its action, keep the circuit ready for building into Project 2.

Open-loop circuits are described in Chapters 2 to 5 and are completely satisfactory for many control applications. In the Appendix (p. 197) is a summary table of open-loop circuits which will help you choose a circuit for a given project.

Monitoring the Output

Fortunately most open-loop control systems are not really open-loop because there is a person at hand to notice if things are amiss and to correct the situation. The engineer, no matter how deeply absorbed in a task, is sure to notice eventually that the workshop is excessively cold or hot. Then the engineer will turn on an extra heater bar or switch off the heater altogether, whatever is appropriate. The same idea applies to tuning a radio set. If the radio goes out of tune because of changes in transmission conditions or in component values in the receiver, the user readjusts the tuning knob until the station is heard perfectly again. If the car engine is idling too fast or too slow, a slight turn of the fuel control valve puts the matter right. In all of these examples, the flow of control has been returned to the input side of the system. The loop has been *closed*, producing what is known as a *closed loop system*. Figure 1.4 shows the closed loop system of the workshop, in which the engineer has become part of the system. By being aware of the temperature and switching the heater on or off accordingly, the engineer becomes part of the closed control loop.

Figure 1.4 illustrates several important features of closed-loop systems, which we will discuss in terms of trying to keep the workshop at a comfortable temperature. On arriving in the workshop first thing in the morning, the engineer has a clear idea of what is considered to be a comfortable temperature. This may be expressed in vague terms, such as 'cosy' or in precise terms such as '25°C'. However the desired level is expressed, and with whatever precision, we refer to this as the *set point*, or *reference point*. It is the temperature to which the

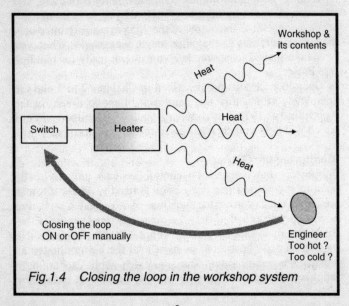

Fig.1.4   Closing the loop in the workshop system

workshop should be brought.   When the engineer enters the room, it is either too cold, just right, or too warm.   In other words, the engineer compares the actual temperature with the set point. The response is straightforward: if the workshop is too cold, turn the heater on; if it is at just the right temperature, do nothing; if the room is too hot, ignore the heater and open the window.   The essence of this is that the *output* of the system (the room temperature) is compared with the set point and an error signal (too cold, just right, too hot) is generated to specify the *difference* between what is required and what is actually occurring.   The nature of the error signal determines the engineer's action.

Project 2 – Demonstrating the Error Signal

The aim of the project is to make the motor of Project 1 turn at a definite speed. Before we can attempt this we must devise a way of deciding when the motor is turning at one particular speed. For this demonstration we use an extremely simple method, a *stroboscope*. A stroboscope consists of a disc with alternate black and white segments. Figure 1.5 shows a stroboscope disc which has two white segments alternating with two black segments, though stroboscopic discs usually have more segments than this. When the disc is spinning in daylight, the segments blur to the eye but, if the disc is illuminated by the light from a mains filament lamp, the stroboscopic effect occurs. At certain rates of revolution the pattern on the disc appears to turn slowly, to be stationary or to turn backward. We see the same effect with a cinema film of the spokes of a carriage wheel. If the disc in Figure 1.5 is spinning at 25 revolutions per second (30 revolutions per second in USA), the segments appear to be stationary. They appear blurred but the effect is clear. It also occurs when the disc is spinning faster, in multiples of 25 revolutions per second.

Copy Figure 1.5 on to a sheet of thin card, glue this to a small block of rubber and push this on to the spindle of the motor. Shine a mains lamp on it. Switch on the power and adjust VR1 until the stroboscopic pattern is visible. If the pattern is turning in the direction that the disc is spinning in,

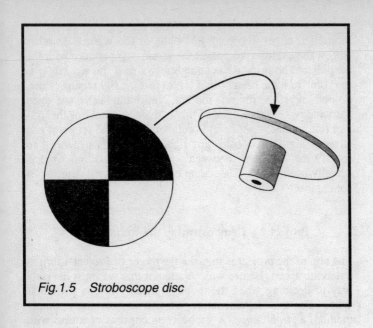

Fig.1.5   Stroboscope disc

the motor is running faster than 25 rps. If it appears to be turning backward, the motor is running slower than 25 rps. Adjust the motor until the pattern appears to be stationary; now the motor is running at exactly 25 rps. The *error signal* in this demonstration is the motion of the pattern. You are in the position of the engineer adjusting the temperature of the workshop. Every time you see the pattern move you re-adjust VR1 to try to keep the pattern stationary. You are part of a closed-loop system, keeping the disc rotating at constant speed.

You will probably find that it is almost impossible to keep the pattern absolutely still. As long as the pattern itself rotates only 2 or 3 times per second, you are holding the speed to within 2 or 3 revolutions of 25 rps. Try to keep it within these limits. Then add a little extra load to the motor by gently touching a screwdriver blade against the edge of the disc. The pattern commences to rotate backwards showing that the existing setting of VR1 no longer gives the required speed. Re-adjust VR1 until the pattern is nearly stationary again. Unless you watch the pattern carefully and make adjustments continually, the motor is unlikely to rotate at the correct speed for long.

Feedback

Figure 1.6, which is based on Figure 1.4 illustrates some more features of a closed-loop system. Most of the output from the heater goes to heating the room and its contents. This is, after all, the prime reason for having a heater in the workshop. But a *small part* of the output is used for control purposes. This is the small amount of heat that reaches temperature sensors in the engineer's skin. The amount of heat involved is a very small fraction of the total output but it is enough for the engineer to become aware of the room temperature and to decide if it is too cold, just right, or too hot. The engineer then reaches out and turns the switch on or off, an action which is referred to as *feedback*. We say that the system has a *feedback loop*.

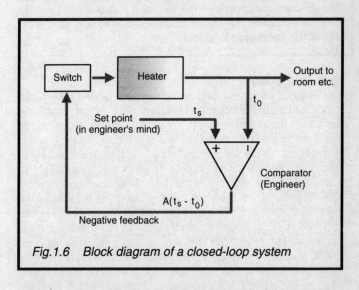

Fig.1.6   Block diagram of a closed-loop system

Let us look more closely at the feedback. The engineer's mind acts as a *comparator*, subtracting the actual (output) temperature t_o from the set point temperature t_s. The difference $(t_s - t_o)$ is the error signal, which may be positive or negative.

9

If it is positive (= too cold), the engineer switches the heater on to make the room *less* cold. If the result is negative (= too hot) the engineer switches the heater off to make the room *less* hot. Feedback is always aimed at making the temperature change in the direction *opposite* to that in which it is drifting. The result is that the workshop temperature remains close to the set point. The engineer also acts as an *amplifier*. It requires only a *small* amount of heat energy to make the engineer spend the *much bigger* amount of energy needed to operate the switch. In most feedback loops it is possible to identify a comparator and an amplifier. In this example the engineer performs both functions.

The same principles applies to the practical demonstration of motor speed control. You watch the pattern, *compare* its motion with the set point (that the pattern should be stationary) and *adjust* VR1 to bring about a change in the *opposite* direction. The direction is opposite so the feedback is *negative*. You also act as an amplifier, for your eyes are sensitive to very slow rotation of the stroboscopic pattern.

Automatic Control

The function of the engineer in the negative feedback loop can easily and more effectively be taken over by an automatic device similar to that shown in Figure 1.7. The essential part of this is a bimetallic strip, made from two different metals welded together. Often we use two alloys such as brass and Invar steel. The two metals are chosen so as to vary appreciably in their coefficients of linear expansion. As temperature increases or decreases, the brass expands or contracts more than the Invar steel. One end of the strip is fixed but the other end is free and moves as the temperature changes. In the figure the brass has expanded more than the steel, causing the strip to bend down. When the strip cools, the brass contracts more than the steel. The strip becomes straighter and, at a certain temperature, touches the contact. This completes a circuit, which switches the heater on. Later, when the room has warmed, the strip bends away from the contact, turning the heater off. The setting of the screw contact determines the set point temperature at which the heater is turned on and off. The contact usually has

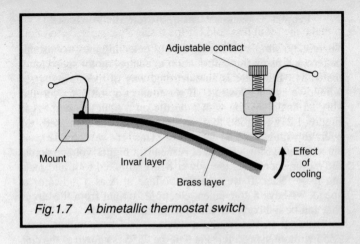

Fig.1.7 *A bimetallic thermostat switch*

Labels in figure: Adjustable contact, Mount, Invar layer, Brass layer, Effect of cooling

a graduated scale so that it can be set by the engineer to any required temperature, after which the bimetallic strip (or *thermostat*) switches the heater on or off automatically.

The operating parts of a bimetallic strip thermostat are entirely mechanical. There are many other instances of purely mechanical closed-loop control systems. One of the earliest to be invented was James Watt's centrifugal governor, used for controlling the speed of steam engines. It remained in use for nearly 200 years for controlling speeds of rotation in many other kinds of machine, including the turntables of gramophone record players. Another purely mechanical system, one that is still widely used today, is the ball-cock system for controlling water level in cisterns. These systems have been perfectly satisfactory in use but for various reasons many of them have been replaced by electronic systems, the subject of this book. Electronics makes possible forms of control that could not be realised mechanically, except at great expense. In the extreme, we can control robots so well by electronics that, far from requiring a human operator, they can mimic the actions of humans with almost unbelievable realism. But, even in the most complex of electronic systems, the fundamental principles of set point, negative feedback, comparison and error signal still apply.

11

Project 3 – Demonstrating Automatic Feedback

There is no simple electronic way of detecting the stroboscope pattern and using this information to control motor speed automatically. But there is an electronic way of measuring speed which we can use instead. If we connect a voltmeter (preferably an analogue one with a needle on a scale) to point A in Figure 1.2 we notice that, as motor speed is increased, the average voltage reading decreases. This is as we should expect since a decreasing voltage at A means a bigger voltage across the motor, increasing the power being supplied to it and making it go faster. If we take the voltage at A as a indicator of speed, we have a convenient electronic output from the circuit that can be fed back for use in automatic control.

The next step is to find a way to control the output of the 7555 without using VR1. Pin 5 of the 7555 is known as the *control* input. Normally we leave this input unconnected but, if we apply a voltage to it, the timing of the device changes. As the voltage is increased the length of the high pulse increases. The effect of this is that motor speed increases. This is ideal for negative feedback. Suppose that the motor is running at constant speed and suddenly an extra mechanical load is applied to slow it down. As it begins to slow down, the voltage at A increases. If we feed an increased voltage to the control input of the 7555, the pulses become longer and so supply more power to the motor. This acts to restore the speed to its former rate. The reverse happens if the load is reduced. Speed increases, the voltage at A falls (and so does the voltage at pin 5), pulse width is reduced and the motor regains its set speed.

In practice, the change in voltage at A is not enough to bring about the desired effect. We need to *amplify* the voltage changes, for which purpose we use an operational amplifier (Fig.1.8). This is a variable-gain amplifier, with VR2 being used to set the gain to a suitable level. Adjusting the gain alters the output voltage from the op amp, so VR2 could also be used as a speed control, but that is not its function. Instead, first disconnect the op amp output from pin 5 of the 7555; on a breadboard just pull out the connecting wire. This opens the loop and there is no feedback. Next use VR1 to set the speed to produce an approximately stationary pattern. Then replace the

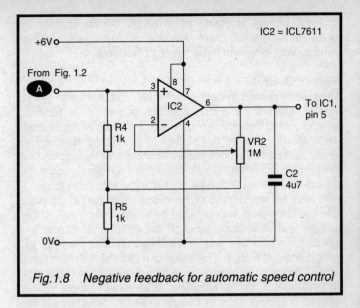

Fig.1.8   Negative feedback for automatic speed control

connection between point A and pin 5. Making this connection
introduces the feedback voltage into the loop, which inevitably
alters the speed. Adjust VR2 until the speed is approximately
correct again; this sets the gain of the op amp to about the right
level. Finally use VR1 to set the speed exactly. With feedback
in operation, motor speed is usually much steadier than before.
It can be left to run indefinitely without further attention.

With feedback in operation the effect of changing the load
(touching the edge of the disc) is not as great as it is without
feedback. But with most simple motors and with no gearing,
even a light load has a relatively big effect. Speed is main-
tained better with feedback but there is usually not the extra
power available to maintain the full speed. If you have an
oscilloscope connected to pin 3 of the 7555, you will see pulse
width automatically increasing in an attempt to maintain speed
when extra load is applied, but perhaps not being able to bring
it back to full speed.

Feedback is specially beneficial if the motor is being run at
low speed. As the motor gets near to stalling and slows down,

13

feedback rapidly increases pulse length, so accelerating the motor. It runs much more smoothly at slow speeds, without stalling, than it does in the absence of feedback.

Remote Control

The remote control system of a TV set or stereo audio system usually involves the human operator as part of the feedback loop, choosing the channel, altering the volume of the sound or the colour-balance of the picture to match the favoured set point. Similarly a model plane owner controls their plane from the ground, using the visual signal from the plane, correcting the effects of wind and avoiding collision with other planes or with trees by sending the appropriate radio signal to the plane. The feedback loop is completed by vision and by radio. Thus remote control systems have all the features of closed loop systems, even though part of the loop may take the form of a pulsed beam of infra-red radiation or a radio signal. The nature of the channel or channels by which the loop is closed make little difference to the operation of the control loop. Remote control is another facet of control systems. We shall not deal specifically with remote control in this book because the subject is already covered in the author's *Practical Remote Control Projects* (Bernard Babani (publishing) Ltd, Book number BP413).

Proportional Control

The engineer reaches the workshop on a cold winter's morning and finds that the temperature is close to zero. It would make little sense to switch on one bar of the heater and wait until the room eventually became comfortable to work in. The obvious course is to switch on both bars of the heater to warm the room quickly, and to keep only one bar on once the comfortable temperature has been attained. In other words, the corrective action is *proportional* to the error signal. The more the actual temperature is below the required temperature, the more bars (and possibly additional heaters) the engineer switches on. The more the actual temperature is above the required temperature, the more windows and doors the engineer flings open. This is known as *proportional control*, and various forms of this are discussed in Chapter 9.

If the engineer leaves the heater switched fully on (both bars) until the workshop has reached the comfortable temperature, and only then turns the second bar off, the second bar remains hot enough to provide a significant amount of heat for a while longer. The room becomes far too hot. With precise proportional control the rate of heating is reduced as the temperature nears the set point. The temperature *approaches* the set point at a gradually decreasing rate, without *overshooting*, and eventually reaches it. This is something that the engineer would probably not spare the time to attend to, but which can be accomplished by suitable electronic circuits or the programming of a microcontroller (Chapter 11).

The situation is similar if the heater is too powerful for the room and is operated by a simple thermostat switch. A large heater continues to supply heat after it has been switched off. Instead of a steady temperature, the room is alternately too hot and too cold. The key to this effect is the *delay* in the system. Delay may also be caused by having the thermostat switch on one side of the room and the heater on the other, or if the air of the room is not able to circulate freely around the bimetallic strip or other heat sensor. It takes appreciable time for the heated air to warm the switch or cold air to cool the switch, and the room becomes excessively hot or cold in the meantime. Such a system is far from ideal, and ways of avoiding this kind of situation must be considered when designing a control system. It reminds us that a closed loop system, although it may be fast and accurate when compared with an open loop system, may have unsuspected complications. It may be subject to instability and other malfunctions if not properly designed.

Regulation and Servo Control
There is a certain amount of overlap between these two concepts but they have distinctive features. Regulation implies using a closed loop system to control a variable so as to hold it as close as possible to a fixed value, the set point. The examples that we have considered, such as the thermostat in the workshop or the speed control of Project 3, are both examples of regulation. With a servo control, or *servomechanism*, the set point is changing frequently and the mechanism is designed so as to follow or track these changes. An example is the system

used to control the position of a robot arm. At any instant the desired position of the arm is specified by a number of variables. The motors or pistons that drive the arm are actuated so as to bring the arm to the desired position or temporary set point. At each stage of the motion, the actual position is compared with the desired position by a feedback system, and control signals are modified accordingly. A closed loop system is used and the output of the servomechanism is mechanical. Because a closed loop system is being used, the robot is able to respond to unforeseeable variations, such as variability in the mass of the objects it is handling.

Robot control is also an example of *sequential control* or *scheduling*, in which the robot is scheduled or *programmed* to perform a sequence of tasks, one after another. A less complex example is controlling a washing machine, in which there is a programmed sequence of heating the water to the correct temperature, soaking, washing, rinsing, pumping out, and spinning. Some of the stages in the sequence, such as the heating of the water, may be subject to closed loop control. Others, such as the spinning for a prescribed period of time at a fixed speed are examples of open loop control.

Analogue and Digital Control
The dynamics of a control system are most often expressed in the form of differential equations. These are a type of mathematical equation which are suited to expressing rates of change and therefore suited to systems in which variables are forever changing (even if the purpose the system is to hold them steady). Circuits based on operational amplifiers are well suited to performing the operations of addition, subtraction and (particularly) differentiation and integration that are basic to differential equations. Operational amplifiers are analogue circuits (circuits with smoothly-changing voltages) and control circuits based mainly on these are referred to as *analogue control circuits*. There are several examples in this book.

With the increasing availability of digital devices such as microcontrollers and microprocessors at reasonable prices, there is a tendency to replace analogue circuits with digital control circuits. If there is any operation more complicated than amplifying and feeding back a signal, it is often easier to use a digital circuit to perform the necessary calculations. Since the actual work of controlling is done by software instead of by hardware, it is much easier to adapt and modify the system. If control is inadequate, it is possible to refine it simply by developing the program further. There is no need to add extra circuit boards and re-wire the connections in order to effect an upgrade, as might be the case with an analogue circuit. Not only are digital circuits able to undertake the functions of an analogue controller but they are specially applicable to sequential control. It would seem that control systems of the future will become almost exclusively digital, which is why this book describes how to use your IBM-PC or one of its equivalents as the basis of a control system. For those who want to build a stand-alone control system, we also explain how to employ an inexpensive microcontroller to operate your electronic project.

Chapter 2

CONTROLLING LAMPS

It makes the design process much more straightforward if we begin by considering the part of the system which is to be controlled, the controlled element. Devices that can be controlled electronically are those powered by an electric current. These include:

* Lamps
* Solenoids
* Relays
* Motors
* Miscellaneous other electrical devices and equipment, such as solid-state sirens, radio receivers, tape players

In this chapter and the next few chapters we look at ways of controlling these different kinds of device, beginning with lamps. Many of the circuits described in this chapter for controlling lamps are equally applicable to switching the other types of electrical device listed above. Full descriptions appear in this chapter and, if applicable, are briefly referred to in the other chapters. The circuits as described in this chapter are all of open-loop design. In later chapters we shall see how to provide feedback so that similar circuits can operate in closed loops. The circuits described in the main body of the chapter are often general-purpose circuit modules that can be applied in a wide variety of ways. To illustrate how to use them, a number of practical control projects are given at the end of the chapter.

Although there are numerous kinds of lamps that we might wish to control, the majority fall into one of three groups with respect to their operating voltage:

6V DC

12V DC

230V AC

The same applies to motors and most of the other electrical devices that we may wish to control. Accordingly, the DC circuits in this book show component values suitable for operating at 6V. Values given in brackets are those required for 12V operation, where they differ. AC circuits are all intended for use with AC mains in the range 200–240V. If it is essential for a controlled element to be run on voltages other than these three, it may be that the circuit will work at that voltage, perhaps after some of the components values or ratings have been altered. If the controlled element has simply to be switched on and off, but will not work at the voltages listed above, switch it with a relay controlled by a 6V or 12V circuit (see Chapter 4).

To keep power requirements as simple as possible, we use only the CMOS 4000 series logic because these ics run on 6V DC. Circuits may conveniently be powered by four 1.5V dry cells in a battery holder. If you are using nickel-cadmium rechargeable cells, which deliver only 1.25V, four such cells deliver 5V. This may not be sufficient for powering certain motors or solenoids, in which case use 5 cells in series, to obtain 6.25V. Alternatively use a mains adapter unit producing 300mA (possibly more) at 6V DC.

Manual Control

The most obvious way of controlling an electric lamp is a mechanical switch. There are many kinds of switch available and it is a good idea when designing a control project to look through the catalogues to find the type that is most suitable. A toggle switch may be the best for certain projects while a slide switch, rocker switch or push-button may be better for others. A push-button may have momentary action, alternate action or latched action. Momentary action buttons may have normally open (most often) or normally closed contacts. For low-voltage circuits a keyboard switch or even a complete key-pad could be suitable. For switching between a set of different functions at low voltage use a rotary switch. Where switching is to be indirect, for example in position detection (see Chapter 3), a micro-switch or a magnetic reed-switch can be employed. For some circuits a touch switch is preferred (see Project 6 at the end of this chapter). An unusual type of switch is used in

20

Project 4.

Whatever type of switch is chosen, the most important point is that the switch must be rated to operate at the voltage and to carry the current that the lamp requires. Lamps are often rated in watts. Given the operating voltage V and the wattage P, the current required is: $I = P/V$. For example, a 12V, 5W lamp requires $5/12 = 0.417$ A. Filament lamps draw a larger current when the lamp is first switched on. This is because the filament is cold and its resistance is less then than when it is hot. With lamps operating at 24V or more, allow about 25% extra current for this.

The brightness of a lamp is most easily controlled by wiring a variable resistor is series with it. Usually the variable resistor is of the rotary type, manually adjusted with a knob. It is also possible for the spindle of a resistor to be rotated mechanically. Ideally, turning the wiper of the resistor from one end of its track to the other should vary the brightness from full illumination to a just-perceptible glow. The correct full-scale value of the resistor is best determined by experiment, since lamps vary so widely in their characteristics, and also the resistance of a lamp depends on the temperature of its filament. As a starting point, calculate the resistance of the lamp when it is running at full brightness. This is found from $R = V/I$ or $R = V^2/P$. For a 6V, 0.3A lamp, $R = 6/0.3 = 20\Omega$. For a 12V, 5W lamp, $R = 12^2/5 = 28.8\Omega$. The variable resistor next above these values makes a starting point for the tests. With most lamps the required resistor value is low, in the range 10Ω to 100Ω. Generally a cermet track resistor is required since these have a higher power rating than carbon-track types and are available in low values covering the 10Ω to 100Ω range. They are rated at various wattages (1W upward), which is essential for lamp-dimming. It is also feasible to use a wire-wound resistor. **It is not recommended to use a variable resistor with AC mains lamps**, except a commercially-made dimming unit rated for the lamp or lamps to be installed. Thyristor dimming circuits for AC lamps are on pages 28–42.

Solid-state Control
Automatic control of lamps requires an indirect method of switching. We can use a relay (Chapter 4) or a solid-state (semi-

conductor) switch. The simplest solid-state circuits use bipolar junction transistors (BJTs) or MOSFETs.

1 Switching with BJTs

Figure 2.1 illustrates some circuits for switching lamps. Figure 2.1a is a circuit for switching a low-voltage filament lamp, such as a torch lamp, a car lamp, a dichroic lamp or a krypton-filled torch lamp, or almost any other device that operates on a low-voltage dc supply. This is a basic transistor switch, using an npn bipolar junction transistor. An analogue or digital control circuit produces a current which flows through R1 to the base of Q1, turning it on. The transistor causes a current appreciably larger than the base current to flow through the lamp. We may make use of this effect in various ways. One of these is to switch a low-voltage lamp by means of a very small current

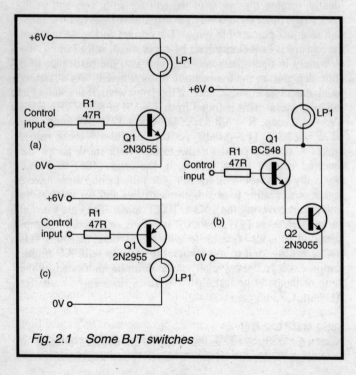

Fig. 2.1   Some BJT switches

that would in itself be insufficient to make the lamp shine. The touch switch circuit of Project 6 makes use of this action. Since so many control operations require digital circuitry it is essential to be able to put lamps and other devices under the control of the output of logic devices. The amount of current available from such an output is limited and, at its greatest, is only enough to illuminate a light-emitting diode (LED). By feeding the output current to a solid-state switch we are able to control lamps and other devices easily. Another way of making use of the current gain of a transistor switch is to switch a large-current or high-voltage device using a low-voltage control circuit. There are fewer applications of this since most high-voltage devices operate on alternating current, which can not be switched by using a transistor. In such cases we may use the transistor switch to control a relay which acts as a switch for the alternating current, as explained in Chapter 4. Alternating current can also be switched by using a thyristor, as explained on page 28.

The lamps listed above mostly operate either on a 6V or a 12V supply, though some torch lamps and krypton-filled lamps run on lower voltages. Normally it is most convenient to run the circuit on 6V or 12V and to choose a lamp of the same or a slightly lower operating voltage. But remember that over-running a lamp appreciably shortens its life.

Some logic ics can not run on a voltage as high as 12V, in which case the logic can be run at 6V and the lamp at 12V (or more) as shown in Figure 2.2. This arrangement can also be used to control lamps of higher voltage, such as 24V. If the lamps are intended for illumination (not simply as indicator lamps) they are usually high-current types and the transistor must be rated to pass a sufficient current. A typical 6V torch lamp requires 0.5A and the equivalent krypton-filled lamp requires 0.65A. The latter gives a far brighter light. Dichroic lamps, which have built-in reflectors, are rated for higher power, and require greater current. For example a 12V dichroic lamp, rated at 50W (but emitting far more light than a mains lamp of the same wattage) requires just over 4A. Car lamps also require high current, a lamp of the type used as a stop light, running at 12V and 20W, requires nearly 2A. Depending on the supply voltage and the current passed by the lamp, the

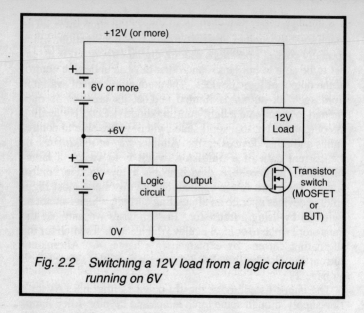

Fig. 2.2   *Switching a 12V load from a logic circuit running on 6V*

transistor may need a heat-sink. However, if the transistor spends most of its time fully off or fully on, it dissipates little power and a heat sink may not be necessary.

The transistor selected for the switch of Figure 2.1a must be able to carry the current which the lamp requires (or two or more times that if two or more lamps are wired in parallel). For most purposes a 2N3055, or MJ15003 transistor is suitable. These are able to pass up to 15A and 20A respectively and have gains of 20-70 and 25-150. If the gain of the transistor is at the lower end of these ranges it may not deliver full power to the lamp when fully switched on. For lower-rated lamps use a TIP31A or BD131 transistor, but note that these transistors have lower gain so are useable only with low-power torch and krypton lamps.   Medium-power and high-power bjt transistors tend to have low gains so that it is not possible to use them to switch lamps from a low-current controller such as the output of a logic gate. The Darlington pair provides large gain. In Figure 2.1b a high-power transistor receives its base current from a low-power transistor. The total gain is well over 1000, so a lamp is easily switched from the output of a logic gate. Two transistors connected as in Figure 2.1b are obtainable in a single package. Examples of power Darlingtons are TIP110 (4A, gain 500), TIP132 (4A, gain 1000), BD679 (6A, gain 2200) and TIP141 (10A, gain 1000). A slight drawback of a Darlington pair is that, since there are *two* base-emitter voltage drops of about 0.6V each, the maximum voltage applied across the lamp is 1.2V less than the supply. Consequently the lamps do not shine at their maximum brightness when the circuit is switched fully on. If maximum brightness is essential, increase the supply voltage, use a lamp rated to run at a lower voltage, or use a relay. A transistor switch with an action the inverse of Figure 2.1a is shown in Figure 2.1c. This uses the complementary pnp transistors, such as a TIP32A or BD132 for current up to 3A, and MJ15004 or 2N2955 for currents up to 20A and 15A.

Any of the switches of Figure 2.1a to c may be used to switch LEDs as indicators. Often the LED is wired in parallel with some other device (such as a motor) as a remote indicator that power is being supplied. In most situations the LED requires a series resistor to limit the current. Typical forward current through an LED is 20mA (though bright LEDs can produce a useful amount of light with less than this). The equation for calculating the value of the resistor is:

$$R = \frac{V_S - 0.6}{I_F}$$

where V_S is the supply voltage and I_F is the forward current. For example, for a 12V supply and a forward current of 20mA (= 0.02A), the resistor required is R = (12 − 0.6)/0.02 = 570Ω. A 560Ω resistor is the nearest suitable value.

By applying a variable voltage to their inputs, the switching circuits in this section and the next may be used to control the brightness of DC lamps. There may be applications for this when the brightness of a lamp is to be controlled by the output from a sensor. When used in this way, the transistor may dissipate an appreciable amount of power, so a heat sink may be essential.

2 Switching with MOSFETs

A n-channel enhancement type MOSFET may be used as a switch as shown in Figure 2.3. Even when switched fully on, a MOSFET has a certain amount of resistance. Although this may be less than 1Ω, it is of the same order of magnitude as the resistance of a lamp filament, so full power is not obtainable. However, the prime advantage of using a MOSFET is the virtually infinite gate impedance. This makes MOSFETs useful for switching lamps from the output of logic gates. Suitable power MOSFETs include VN66AF (2A, 3Ω) IRF510 (4A, 0.6Ω), IRF520 (8A, 0.3Ω) and IRF531 (10A, 0.18Ω). The figures in brackets are the maximum current and the 'on' resistance from source to drain. In general, the higher the power rating, the lower the 'on' resistance.

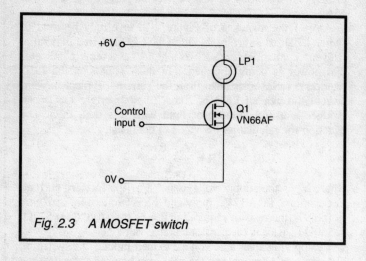

Fig. 2.3   A MOSFET switch

3 Digital Switching

Transistor switching lends itself to control by the outputs of digital circuits. As an example, take the circuit of Figure 2.4. This comprises two NAND gates cross-connected to form a bistable latch. The circuit has two stable states. In either state one gate has a high output and the other has a low output. Pressing push-button S1 makes the output of gate IC1a go high.

26

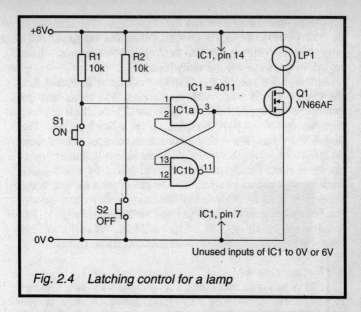

Fig. 2.4   Latching control for a lamp

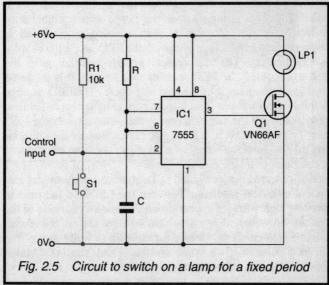

Fig. 2.5   Circuit to switch on a lamp for a fixed period

27

This turns on the transistor and lights the lamp. The lamp stays lit until push-button S2 is pressed, when the output of IC1a goes low. This circuit can also be triggered by low pulses from logical outputs that are normally high.

Although we specify the CMOS 7555 timer in Figure 2.5, the circuit should work with the original 555 timer and the newer low-current 555 timers. In Figure 2.5, the timer is wired as a monostable to switch a lamp on for a fixed period. The dotted lines show the wiring for a manual control, which turns on the lamp when the button is pressed. Without the parts drawn in dotted lines, the circuit is triggered by a low pulse from another digital circuit. The length of time for which the lamp is on is set by the value of the timing resistor and capacitor. For example, if $R = 100k\Omega$ and $C = 220\mu F$, then $t = 1.1RC = 1.1 \times 100 \times 10^3 \times 220 \times 10^{-6} = 24.2s$. A period of this length would be suitable for switching a corridor lamp.

4 Thyristor Control

Thyristors and their associated devices, diacs and triacs, are of most use for controlling AC mains lamps. A very simple ON/OFF switching circuit is illustrated in Figure 2.6. It is suitable for controlling a low-power lamp, heater or other non-inductive device. It uses an opto-coupled triac, which is triggered into conduction whenever the LED inside the coupler is switched on. The triac ceases to conduct at the end of the half-cycle but, if the LED remains switched on, it is triggered again at the beginning of the next half-cycle. The LED requires a minimum of about 20mA to trigger conduction and this is provided when the switch S1 is closed. Alternatively the LED may be switched on by a transistor. The transistor may be controlled also from the output of a logic gate, or from an output of a computer or microcontroller, so here is a way of controlling a mains-powered device digitally. The optocoupler provides sufficient electrical insulation between the LED and the triac to prevent high voltages appearing on the low-voltage side of the circuit. However, this safety feature depends on the circuit being wired correctly. **Before attempting to build any of the circuits described in this section, read the AC Mains Precautions on pages 38–40.**

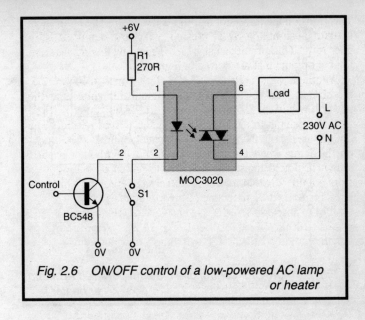

Fig. 2.6   ON/OFF control of a low-powered AC lamp
or heater

The circuit of Figure 2.6 is limited to low currents because it uses the low-power triac of the optocoupler. The current through the triac must not exceed 1.2A. When a lamp is first switched on, the filament is cold and has a much lower resistance than when the lamp is lit. In this circuit, the initial surge of current through the cold filament must not exceed 1.2A. The mains voltage is quoted as 230V, but this is its root mean square value. The amplitude of the mains is actually 325V. This means that the cold resistance of a lamp filament or a heater should not be less than $335/1.2 = 270\Omega$. Lamps used in the home are generally rated at 60W or 100W and have cold filament resistances much lower than this, so this circuit can not be used to control single lamps of this wattage. The circuit is suitable only for lamps of lower wattage, such as 15W, or for two or more lamps of higher wattage wired in series. The heater of a 'slow cooker' or similar low-power heater (or a 15W soldering iron) may have a resistance of about 300Ω, making it possible to use this circuit as an on-off control or as part of a thermostat

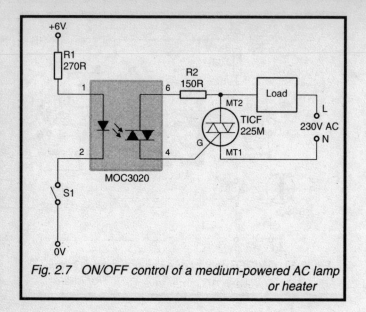

Fig. 2.7   ON/OFF control of a medium-powered AC lamp or heater

system. Figure 2.6 shows the LED of the opto-coupler being switched by a mechanical switch. The figure also shows how to replace the switch with a transistor. An analogue or digital control voltage applied to the base of the transistor is used to turn the LED on or off and thus to trigger the triac. The circuit is energised if the analogue input voltage is high enough to saturate the transistor. In practice it is preferable to use the output of a Schmitt trigger (p. 90). Similarly, a logical high applied to the transistor, causes power to be applied to the load.

For switching lamps or heaters of higher rating, the circuit of Figure 2.7 uses the coupled triac to trigger a triac of higher power. The TICF225M in Figure 2.7 can be used with a load current up to 2A. A heat sink may be needed. Like Figure 2.6, this circuit too can be controlled either by a mechanical switch or (through a transistor) by analogue or digital inputs.

In Figure 2.8 the triac is triggered into conduction at a variable stage in each half-cycle, depending on the setting of VR1. This means that the brightness of the lamp may be varied from nil to full brilliance. The maximum load is 100W, but could be

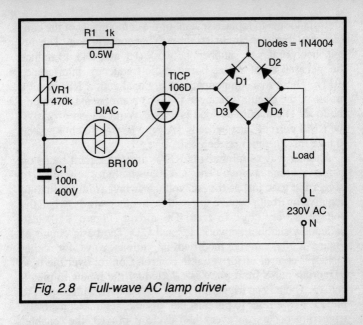

Fig. 2.8 Full-wave AC lamp driver

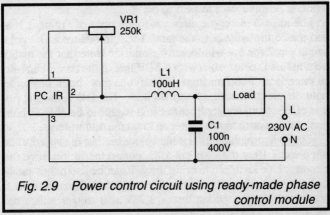

Fig. 2.9 Power control circuit using ready-made phase control module

increased by using diodes and a thyristor of higher wattage. Another manually adjusted brightness control is shown in Figure 2.9. This uses a ready made thick-film hybrid phase control module to replace several of the components of the conventional thyristor circuit, so simplifying construction. The circuit incorporates a 'snubber' network (L1 and C1), to reduce the generation of mains-borne radio-frequency interference (RFI). These two components are optional and, if RFI is not a problem, the circuit is reduced to just 3 components, including the load. The maximum load is 250W. With a load of 250W, the RMS current just exceeds 1A, so a miniature choke rated to take this current may be used.

Another way of minimising RFI is to use a circuit based on a *zero-voltage switch*. The CA3059 includes circuitry to trigger the triac just as the AC voltage swings from positive to negative or from negative to positive, in other words, when the voltage is very close to zero. The circuit (Figure 2.10) also includes a snubber network, R2 and C3. The basic circuit of Figure 2.10a can be modified in various ways for either ON/OFF control or for variable control. Control over the triac triggering pulse from pin 4 is effected by the inputs to pins 9 and 13. There is no triggering if pin 9 is positive with respect to pin 13, so we refer to pin 9 as the 'disable' input. Conversely, triggering occurs on every half-cycle if pin 13, the 'enable' input, is positive with respect to pin 9.

The mains side of the circuit is to the right of Figure 2.10a, and the control side is to the left. The ic produces a DC voltage at pin 2 for use with control circuits. Note that the mains neutral line is continuous with the 0V line of the control circuit, so there is no isolation from the mains in this circuit unless an opto-coupler is used, as described later. The DC voltage at pin 2 is 6.5V. In many applications it is useful to be able to hold one of the control inputs (pin 9 or 13) at the mid-voltage, 3.25V. Fig 2.10b shows that this is done by connecting the appropriate pin to pins 10 and 11. If pin 13 is connected in this way, the circuit can be switched to bring the voltage at pin 9 either above or below the mid-voltage, as in Figure 2.10c. When the switch is closed, pin 9 is pulled below 3.25V and trigger pulses are enabled; the load is energised.

The CA3059 may also be controlled through an opto-coupler, as in Figure 2.10d. A wide range of analogue or digital circuits may be used to turn on the LED. The 0V line of the LED circuit is not connected to the 0V/neutral line of the

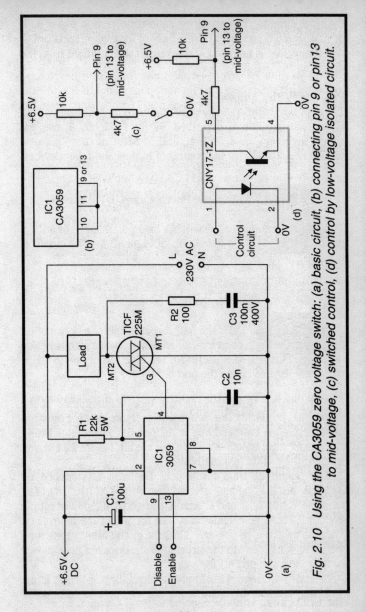

Fig. 2.10 Using the CA3059 zero voltage switch: (a) basic circuit, (b) connecting pin 9 or pin13 to mid-voltage, (c) switched control, (d) control by low-voltage isolated circuit.

33

CA3059 circuit. The specified opto-coupler is a 6-pin d.i.l. device. Pin 6 is connected to the base of the phototransistor but this connection is not used in this circuit so is omitted from the diagram.

Projects With Lamps
These projects illustrate some of the many applications of the lamp control circuits described in this chapter. These are simple switching or dimming circuits. Most of these projects can also be adapted for the control of motors and other devices.

Project 4 – Automatic Porch Lamp, DC Version

This project automatically switches on a porch lamp for a short period. It is based on the circuit of Figure 2.5. The circuit is triggered in one of two ways:

1 A micro-switch or magnetic switch mounted on the door; the lamp comes on whenever the door is opened.

2 A pressure mat under the hall carpet or under a doormat on the porch; the lamp comes on whenever someone stands beside the door. This is also is useful for security, turning on the light whenever anyone enters the porch.

It is possible to implement both types of switching at the same time, by wiring the switch and pressure mat (or pressure mats, one in the hall and one in the porch) in parallel. Closing any *one* of these switches triggers the circuit. Figure 2.11 shows some of the switching possibilities.

The length of time for which the lamp is switched on depends on the values selected for R and C (p. 28). The required values of R and C are unaffected by the power supply voltage. The time calculated is that for which the lamp is on after the switch is re-opened. Thus the circuit allows time for a visitor to walk away to the street after the door has been closed or they have stepped off the mat.

Selecting a lamp: This application requires a bright lamp. Tungsten halogen filament lamps are available rated at 4.4W

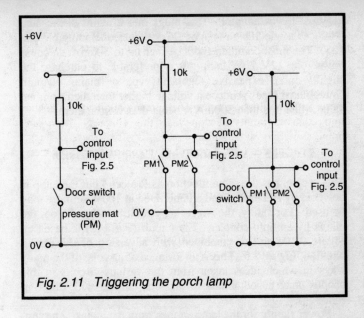

Fig. 2.11   Triggering the porch lamp

running on a 5.2V supply. Allowing for the voltage drop across the switching transistor, these would give their maximum light output with a 6V circuit supply. For greater illumination, use a 10W tungsten halogen lamp running on 12V. For maximum brightness use a 12V dichroic lamp of 20W or 50W. Special fittings are available to take these lamps. Whatever type of lamp is decided upon, check how much current it passes and make sure that the transistor is rated to pass an equal or preferably greater current.

Power supply: One point to be considered before beginning construction is the nature of the power supply. A 12V 20W lamp takes 0.24A. An alkaline D cell has a capacity of 14Ah. Therefore a 12V battery of 8 D cells delivers 0.24A for 14/0.24 = 58 hours. It is feasible to use such a battery, or to use two 6V lantern cells wired in series. Rechargeable nickel-cadmium cells are cheaper to run but have lower capacity than alkaline cells so they need re-charging frequently. For example a ni-cad D cell has a capacity of 4Ah, so a battery would need recharging after 16 hours of use. The most economical supply is a low-cost mains adaptor. This plugs into a mains socket and produces a selectable range of DC voltages, including 6V and 12V. The most common types deliver up to 300mA, so could power one 12V 20W lamp. It is preferable to purchase the slightly more expensive regulated type of mains adaptor. Unregulated types produce a voltage higher than their nominal value when less than 300mA is being drawn from them.

Project 5 – Automatic Porch Lamp, AC Version

This project has the same function as Project 4 but the lamp is powered by AC mains, and a lamp rated at 100W or more may be used. For safety, the triggering circuit is isolated from the mains by an opto-coupler. The circuit (Fig.2.12) is based on Figure 2.10a and d, combined with a version of the timing circuit of Figure 2.5. This is an instance of just one of the many ways in which ideas taken from the various circuits in this chapter may be combined to produce circuits with differing functions.

Power supply for the lamp comes from the mains. The supply for the transistor side of the optocoupler comes from pin 2 of IC2. The timer circuit requires very little current (only $200\mu A$ when not triggered) which is best supplied by a 6V alkaline battery. A battery of four size AAA cells will last for up to a year running 12 hours per day. .

Before planning construction, read the advice given on pages 38–40 concerning AC Mains Precautions.

The project is to be housed in a metal or plastic case; in many ways, a plastic case is to be preferred since this avoids risks of the enclosure accidentally becoming live. Also, the inside walls of many brands of plastic enclosure have slots into which a circuit-board may conveniently be slipped. The enclosure must be large enough to hold the circuit board and a 4-cell AAA battery holder. Bolt a mains socket to the underside of the enclosure (Fig.2.13) and mount the circuit-board and the battery switch on the lid. A socket for the lead to the triggering switch is mounted on the side of the enclosure in a suitable position. This must not be a mains socket, but one of the many types of low-voltage socket available. The simplest solution is

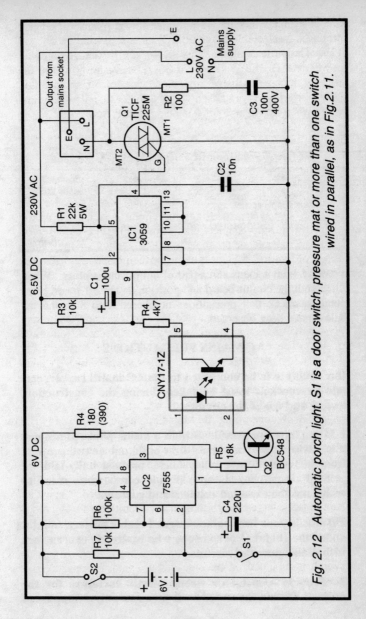

Fig. 2.12   Automatic porch light. S1 is a door switch, pressure mat or more than one switch wired in parallel, as in Fig.2.11.

37

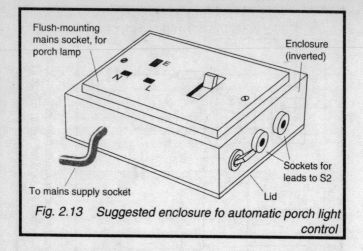

Flush-mounting mains socket, for porch lamp

Enclosure (inverted)

Sockets for leads to S2

To mains supply socket

Lid

Fig. 2.13   Suggested enclosure fo automatic porch light control

a pair of 4mm sockets and a pair of 4mm banana plugs. When laying out the circuit-board and positioning the off-board components, check that precautions numbered 4 to 8 in the list below have been observed.

AC MAINS PRECAUTIONS

If a circuit is to be connected to the AC mains supply, certain precautions must be taken during the construction, testing and use of the circuit:

1 If you have not previously built a mains-powered project, it is advised that you should first build one or two projects from kits which have ready-made, professionally-laid-out printed circuit boards and include components rated to withstand the expected voltages and currents.

2 If this is your first home-designed mains project, build it under the guidance of someone who is already experienced with mains-powered circuits.

3   Provide a metal or strong plastic enclosure for the project. Obtain the enclosure from a recognised supplier of

electronics components. Do not use plastic 'sandwich boxes' or other non-electronic boxes; they may easily shatter or may be a fire risk.

4 Take special care with the layout of the circuit board and the mounting of off-board components. Try to confine all components and tracks which carry mains current to one area of the board. Make all mains-carrying tracks as short as possible, using mains-rated insulated wire to carry mains current between terminals on different parts of the board.

5 If the enclosure is made of metal, connect the Earth line of the mains supply to it.

6 Secure the mains cable with a cable clip to the inside of the enclosure, close to the point where it enters the enclosure.

7 Construction should be as robust as possible; bear in mind that at some stage the project may be dropped or suffer mechanical damage. It must be able to withstand rough handling.

8 Check that no bare metal parts or tracks that are conducting mains current can come into contact with bare metal parts or tracks that are intended to be at low voltage. Check that this can not happen if the project is dropped or distorted. It sometimes happens that a project looks safe in this respect when first mounted in the enclosure, but screwing down the lid brings bare metal parts into contact with each other, especially if a mass of bunched-up connecting wires forces the circuit-board out of alignment.

9 Before plugging the circuit into the mains, use a magnifier to check the circuit board for streaks or blobs of solder that may be short-circuiting adjacent tracks. On a stripboard, use a magnifier to check that strips that should have been cut across have actually been completely cut. Look to see that there is no thin 'wire' of copper remaining around the rim of the hole, and that there are no flakes of copper still attached which short-circuit to adjacent tracks. Use a

continuity checker to confirm that all points on the circuit that should be connected are in fact connected. Also confirm that there are no short circuits between the mains lines and between the mains lines and the low-voltage lines of the circuit.

10 If there are any sections of the circuit that can be tested without connecting the circuit to the mains, test these sections first.

11 Before plugging the circuit into the mains make a final check on the circuit comparing it point by point with the circuit diagram. Bolt the lid of the enclosure fully into place.

12 When all is correct to the best of your knowledge, test the circuit with mains power switched on. If any faults become apparent, switch off the mains supply immediately. Do not open the enclosure until you have switched off the mains supply and removed the mains plug from the socket.

13 If you have re-opened the enclosure to investigate faults, replace the lid and bolt it in place before reconnecting the circuit to the mains.

14 As an ADDITIONAL precaution (but not to be observed instead of the precautions listed above) take the mains supply from a socket equipped with a residual current device (RCD).

Project 6 – A Touch-Operated Bedside Lamp

A low-voltage DC lamp is suitable for this project. If the lamp is to be used for only an hour or so nightly, it may be powered by a battery. Otherwise, a mains adapter should be used (p. 36). The circuit is controlled by a touch-switch consisting of three metal pads close together (Fig.2.14). When the gap between the central pad and one of the pads is bridged by touching a finger against them, a minute current flows through the finger-tip from an outer pad to the central pad. If the finger bridges the ON pad and central pad, the input of the first NAND gate in made high and its output goes low. This is inverted by the second gate, the output of which goes high, turning on the transistor switch. In addition a current is fed back through R1 to hold the central pad high after the finger is removed. The capacitor helps stabilise the circuit in this state. The circuit stays in this state until it is put into the inverse state by bridging the gap between the OFF plate and the central plate. Q1 is a low-power transistor capable of passing 270mA, so the lamp must have a suitably low power rating. The project is housed in a plastic enclosure, which could be decorated if the lamp is for a young child's bedroom.

Project 7 – Lamp Dimmer

This is a triac-based open-loop control circuit which has many uses as a dimmer for a table-lamp, a bedside reading lamp or for producing subtle lighting effects in the living-room. It may also be used as a motor speed control for low-power ac electric motors, such as those used in desk-top fans. Before planning construction study the AC MAINS PRECAUTIONS on pages 38–40.

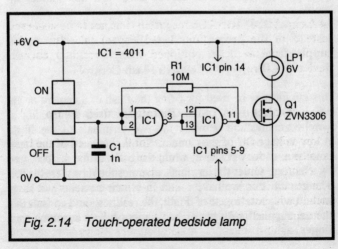

Fig. 2.14   Touch-operated bedside lamp

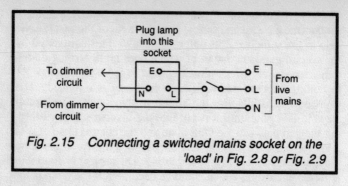

Fig. 2.15 Connecting a switched mains socket on the
'load' in Fig. 2.8 or Fig. 2.9

The project may be based on one of the circuits in Figures 2.8 or 2.9. Although the PC1 phase controller of Figure 2.9 is fairly expensive, it requires less wiring. The circuit is housed in a plastic box, as in Figure 2.13. If a switched mains socket is used (Fig.2.15), the switch turns the whole circuit off when the lamp is not in use. Mount VR1 on the side of the enclosure. Although the table lamp that it is intended for use with the project may not have an Earth lead, it is advisable from the point of view of safety to use 3-core wire for the connection to the mains socket and to wire this to the Earth terminal of the project's output socket. This will provide a earthed connection for any other device that may be used with the dimmer in future.

Project 8 – Camera Flash Control

This circuit may be used for firing the flash of a camera or an individual flash unit. Most flashes are fired by making a switched connection between the two terminals of the flash socket on the body of the camera. Often this has a central terminal pin, usually positive, while the body of the socket is at 0V. Shorting across the terminals operates the flash. This is the arrangement that we have found in all the cameras we have worked with but, in case of doubt, the reader should consult the manual supplied with his or her camera *before* attaching this project.

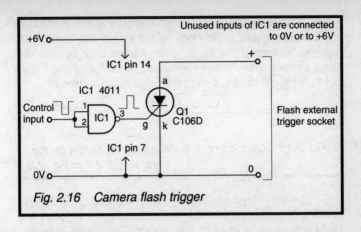

Fig. 2.16   Camera flash trigger

The main purpose of this project is to fire the flash under logical or computer control. The shutter is opened slightly before the photograph is to be taken, then the flash takes the photograph, after which the shutter is closed. Very short exposures may be obtained when using a high-speed flash of duration 1/40000 second. Even without a high-speed flash, striking photographs may be obtained by triggering the flash when a person or animal breaks an infra-red beam crossing the point of focus. Another application is for producing multiple images. For example, the shutter is opened while a person walks across in front of the lens. The flash is triggered at regular intervals, so recording a succession of images on the film. Photographs of this kind are useful for investigations into bodily movement or purely for their decorative merits. An automatic flash device could also have a role in a security system. Finally, the project can be used for firing a slave flash. A sensor detects the light emitted when the camera flash is fired and fires the slave flash almost at the same instant. The logic circuits required for these applications are not detailed here but later chapters on sensors and logical or computer control will help you with designing circuits for many functions.

Instead of using a switch to fire the flash, we use a thyristor (Fig.2.16). The output of the circuit is fed to a plug that fits the flash socket on the camera. Take care to wire the socket with the correct polarity. With most cameras, it is easy to check the polarity of the socket by touching the probes of a multimeter to the central pin and to the body of the socket and reading the voltage between them. Input to the circuit may be provided from a remote push-button (connected as the buttons in Figure 2.14), a logical circuit, a computer, or a microcontroller.

Chapter 3

CONTROLLING SOLENOIDS

A solenoid is a wire coil of several hundred or more turns, its length usually being greater than its diameter. The solenoid usually has an unmagnetised core of soft iron. In one type of solenoid the core may is able to slip easily in or out of the coil. When the coil is not energised, the core is only partly within the coil. When a current is passed through the coil, the strong magnetic field generated draws the core forcibly into the coil. This *linear motion* is transmitted through a coupling to the mechanism which is to be driven. The core may exert either a pulling or a pushing force, depending on how it is attached to the mechanism. The action of the solenoid is *not* reversed by reversing the direction of the current. When the current is switched off the core is no longer attracted into the coil, but is not repelled from the coil either. A spring or other counteracting force is needed to restore the core to its original position.

In another type of solenoid, the core is fixed within the coil. Together, they act as an electromagnet. When current is passed through the coil the magnetic field attracts an armature, which is a plate of soft iron and is attached to the mechanism. An electric bell is an example of a mechanism based on this kind of solenoid. A spring or similar mechanism is needed to restore the armature to its original position when the current is switched off. This is the principle of the relay (Chapter 4).

A third type of solenoid has an armature which produces *rotary motion* when it is energised, usually turning a spindle though 45°. This type of solenoid is very expensive and we shall not consider any applications of it.

There are also a number of ready-made devices which incorporate a solenoid. These include door catches, door bolts, and valves. Model railway enthusiasts will be familiar with electrically controlled turnouts, which are based on two-way solenoid action. A wide range of solenoid-operated valves is available suited to controlling the flow of liquids such as water, aqueous solutions and oils, as well as air and gases.

With the exception of the smaller general-purpose types, solenoids tend to be too expensive for regular use by the electronics hobbyist. But it is often possible to remove the solenoids from an old electric bell and use these in conjunction with a piece of soft iron as an armature. A defunct domestic washing-machine is a source of solenoid operated valves. The way to construct home-made solenoids is described in Project 11, at the end of this chapter.

Specially prepared nickel-titanium wire is an interesting functional equivalent of a solenoid in that it produces a pulling force. For this reason, it is included with the solenoids in this chapter.

Solenoid Action

In many applications the solenoid is used to deliver a mechanical impulse by passing a pulse of current through it. Usually solenoids can exert only a *pull* when the core is drawn into the coil. Some have a driving rod which passes through the coil and projects at the other end; this type can deliver a *push*. In short, a solenoid produces *linear motion*. The force exerted by the solenoid depends on the instantaneous current through the coil and the extent to which the core is inside the coil. Force is usually measured in gf (grams-force) or kgf (kilograms force). If the solenoid is placed so that the core moves vertically upward when the coil is energised, a force of 1kgf will *just* hold a mass of 1kg suspended against the force of gravity. The force can also be measured in newton, where $1N = 0.102kgf = 102gf$.

Although some solenoids are designed for pushing and others for pushing, a given solenoid can only push *or* pull. It can not operate forcibly in both directions. If a solenoid is being used for pushing an object, there must be a spring or some other means of restoring the object to its original position when the solenoid is de-energised. Naturally, the force of the spring must be less than that of the solenoid, and the object is returned to its original position with less power. Unfortunately, the effective motion-producing force of the solenoid is reduced by the restoring force of the spring.

The strongest force is obtained by making the current as large as the coil can withstand and by positioning the core well within the coil to begin with. A solenoid rated at 12V may be run at voltages up to 3 times this, with perhaps a six-fold increase in force. The only provision is that the coil must not be excited continuously at the higher voltage. For example, a typical 12V coil may be run at 38V provided that the duty cycle is no more than 10%. The position of the core within the coil is defined by the *stroke*, the distance the core can travel from its initial position to its final position (when it is fully within the coil). For example, a solenoid may exert 50gf if the stroke is 4mm. If the stroke is only 2mm the force rises to 100gf. Thus increased force may be obtained at the expense of reduced stroke.

A solenoid being used to exert an impulsive force is easily controlled by a switching circuit that applies full power for an instant. In addition to its use for impulsive action, a solenoid may be used to exert a continuous force, but controlling the force is relatively difficult. The problem is that the force does not depend entirely on the controlling current. It depends on the extent to which the core has been drawn into the coil, and this relationship is not linear. The situation is inherently unstable. For example, a slight increase in current increases the force slightly, drawing the core a little further into the coil. This change of position causes an increase of force, drawing the core further in. The situation escalates and the core snaps fully into the coil. Any attempt to produce a continuous steady force requires closed-loop control (p. 6), and even with this control is difficult.

Electrical Characteristics
In order to produce sufficient force, the coil of a solenoid usually has low resistance and takes a large current. These coils usually operate on 12V DC, and many are rated at 24V DC or higher. A 12V solenoid running on 6V exerts a diminished though useful pull over a short stroke distance. If only a slight pull is needed, it simplifies the circuit to run the solenoid on 6V instead of having to provide 12V specially for the solenoid. There are also industrial solenoids operating on 230V AC. In this chapter we describe circuits for 12V solenoids and show how to modify them for working on 24V. We also describe some circuits for boosting the voltage to higher levels to operate a solenoid at higher voltage for a short duty cycle.

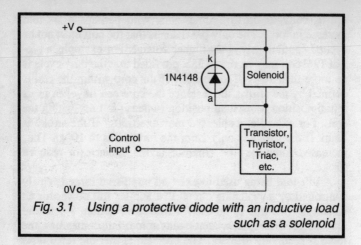

*Fig. 3.1   Using a protective diode with an inductive load
such as a solenoid*

A solenoid is inductive and a consequence of this is that a brief back emf is generated when the coil is switched off and the magnetic field decays. The size of the emf depends on the rate at which the field decays which, at switching off, is almost instantaneous. This means that the back emf may be many times greater than the voltage being applied to the coil when it was energised. It can amount to several hundred volts in the reverse direction. Voltage spikes of this kind may easily damage transistors and other electronic devices in the driving circuit. Damage is prevented by wiring a diode as shown in Figure 3.1. The diode conducts away the current that is produced by the back emf.

Much of the discussion and many of the circuits of Chapter 2 apply equally to solenoids. The reader is referred to the information on switches (p. 22) and to the circuits illustrated in Figs 2.1 to 2.5. To use these circuits for a solenoid, substitute a 12V solenoid for the lamp and run the circuit on 12V. Ensure that the transistor is rated to pass the current required by the solenoid. Add a protective diode to the circuit as in Figure 3.1.

Increasing the Force
Figure 3.2 shows a circuit for a voltage doubler based on the 7660 voltage converter ic. The voltage is not fully doubled for the voltage-drop of the two diodes has to be subtracted. These

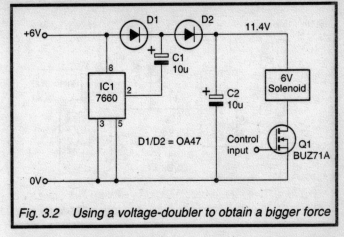

Fig. 3.2   Using a voltage-doubler to obtain a bigger force

are germanium diodes so the voltage drop of each is about 0.2V, and the output of the circuit is 11.6V. If the rest of the control circuit is operating on 6V, the voltage doubler allows a 12V solenoid to be operated on almost full power. This voltage doubler can accept a supply voltage up to 10.5V, giving an output of just over 20V. A 12V solenoid driven by this output will deliver a more powerful force, but remember that the solenoid must not be switched on continuously. A duty cycle of no more than 25% is recommended.

The versatile 7555 timer is the basis for the voltage doubler illustrated in Figure 3.3. Since this ic is rated to run at up to 15V, it may be used to produce a voltage of up to 30V. This can be used to drive a 24V solenoid or to obtain greater force from a 12V solenoid. In the latter case the duty cycle must not exceed 15%.

Using Solenoids
The features of solenoid action are:

1 They move forcibly in only one direction; an opposing force is required for recovery.
2 It saves current and the risks of overheating if they are in action intermittently.
3 They have a relatively small stroke.

49

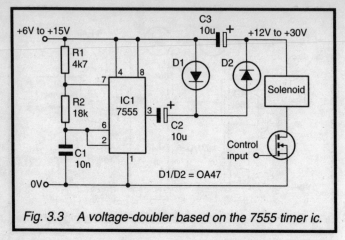

Fig. 3.3   A voltage-doubler based on the 7555 timer ic.

Figure 3.4 illustrates these points. In Figure 3.4a the puppet is made to dance and wave its arms when the solenoids jerk the strings. This illustrates the 'one direction' action. Gravity provides the recovery force. The lever in Figure 3.4b has two opposing solenoids which are energised alternately, moving the lever to the left or to the right. The control circuit must allow only one to be energised at a time. If motion is in the horizontal plane and the mechanism has a reasonable amount of friction, the lever will not move unless it is pulled one way or the other. The solenoids need to be energised only when the lever is to be moved. An arrangement such as this is suitable for a turnout for a model railway and is referred to as a turnout motor. It can also be adapted for moving the rudder of a model boat or plane. One of the solenoids could be replaced by a spring or elastic cord, but then the single solenoid must be strong enough to extend the spring as well as to move the lever. The lever mechanism is also able to produce a limited amount of circular motion. More extensive circular motion is possible with the mechanism in Figure 3.4c A drum has cord wound round it with a mass or extended spring attached to its free end. As the solenoid is energised it pulls up the catch, allowing the drum to rotate. If the solenoid is switched on only for an instant the catch drops and the drum is stopped after one revolution. In Figure 3.4d the trapdoor drops open when the bolt is withdrawn

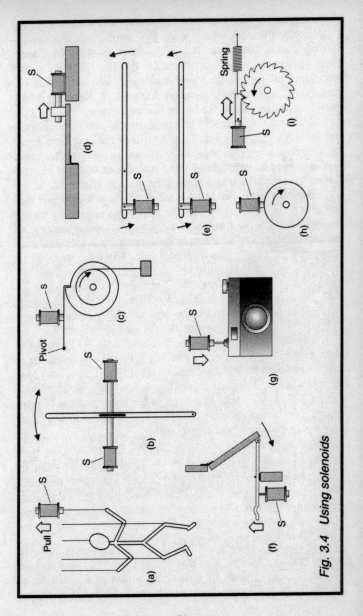

Fig. 3.4 Using solenoids

51

by the solenoid. The door is closed and re-bolted manually.

The principle of levers is used in Figure 3.4e. The upper drawing shows how to use a lever to magnify the stroke, and allow motion over a greater distance. But the force is correspondingly reduced. In the lower drawing the effective stroke is diminished, with a corresponding increase in force. In both these mechanisms there are losses due to friction.

When designing solenoid mechanisms it is often possible to arrange for a relatively small movement of the core to trigger off or release energy previously stored in the mechanism. Figure 3.4d is an example of this. Another example is Figure 3.4f which shows how to arrange for a window (for example, in a greenhouse) to be closed by a solenoid. In this example the solenoid is being used to push. The window is opened by hand, raising it against the force of gravity and so storing energy in the mechanism. The window is held open by a conventional perforated strip resting on a vertical peg. When the solenoid is energised, it pushes the strip up, off the peg. This small movement releases the energy stored in the opened window. Gravity pulls it down and it finishes in a vertical position. Another example of pushing action is the camera shutter release shown in Figure 3.4g. This is the mechanism used in Project 9.

A solenoid may be used to prevent motion, as in Figure 3.4h. Here a drum is rotating and a braking action is applied using a solenoid to push its armature against the drum. This is only one of many ways in which a braking action may be arranged. Figure 3.4i shows a simple though rather noisy method of producing continuous circular motion. The solenoid is activated repeatedly and the wheel slowly turns.

There are so many mechanisms that can be driven by a solenoid or a pair of solenoids that it is impossible to illustrate them all here. The exact details must depend on the application, but it is hoped that the ideas behind the examples given here will be of help.

Flexinol Wire

This wire, also known as 'Muscle Wire', contracts forcibly when heated through a relatively short temperature range. Heating is easily done by passing a current of a few tens or hundreds of milliamps through the wire. Depending on the gauge of the wire, forces of several hundred grams-force are obtainable, with a maximum of about 1 kgf. When the current is switched off and the wire cools it recovers its original length. This wire has many applications and can replace solenoids in many situations. The Electronic Piston is a device with related properties.   Its normal length is 100mm but it contracts to 76mm with a force up to 450gf when a current of 5A is passed through it.

Flexinol wire and the Electronic Piston can replace a solenoid in many situations and are controllable by most circuits intended for switching solenoids. The protective diode is not required. See the Appendix for suppliers.

Projects With Solenoids
The examples in Figure 3.4 may suggest possible projects to the reader. Here we follow up four ideas in more detail.

Project 9 – Camera Shutter Release 1

The principle is shown in Figure 3.4g and may be used with cameras that have a shutter release button that is pressed to trigger the shutter. For cameras with a remote release socket use a relay, as in Project 14 in the next chapter. Project 9 requires a solenoid designed for pushing. The core has a narrow rod attached to it and this projects beyond the bottom end of the coil. The core is partly out of the coil to begin with. When current flows, the core is drawn a little way into the coil, so making the rod project further, pushing against the shutter release button.

The camera is held in a wooden cradle, the design of which depends very much on the exact shape of the camera. The solenoid is mounted on the cradle so that it is vertically above the camera with the projecting rod resting loosely on the button, as in Figure 3.4g. The circuit can be any one of those suggested earlier in the chapter. It is not usually necessary to use a voltage doubler.

Project 10 – Flag Waver

This is an attention-attracting warning device which has applications when it is not practicable to run wires between the sensor and a indicator lamp or buzzer. In many countries the postman does not push the mail through a slot in the front door but places it in a mailbox situated by the front gate. Newspapers are left there too. It is often not possible to see from the house if any mail has been delivered and the mailbox is often too far away from the house to make it practicable to run a wire between the mailbox and the house. When this project is triggered by the arrival of mail, it waves a flag to and fro. The flag is large enough to be clearly visible from the house. A waving flag is easier to see than a flashing lamp, especially in bright sunlight. The flag waves unceasingly until the householder collects the mail and resets the circuit. There are other situations in which a flag-waver has applications. For example it could be connected to the door-bell circuit to give warning that the door-bell has been sounded. The flag continues to wave after the button has been released. A visible indicator of this kind is a benefit when the occupant of the house is deaf. It could also be placed in the window of a house to indicate to neighbours that the elderly or infirm occupant is in need of assistance.

The circuit (Fig.3.5) is based on a bistable circuit built from two NAND logic gates, which is set and reset by a pair of switches. When S1 is closed, even briefly, the output of the flip-flop goes high and enables the astable. This delivers pulses to the transistor which switches the solenoid on and off repeatedly. The flag is on a pendulum which normally hangs as shown in Figure 3.6 but is pulled to one side (dashed lines) when the solenoid is energised. Gravity restores the pendulum to its original position when the solenoid is de-energised. The device is more effective if the rate of switching the solenoid equals the natural frequency of the pendulum, which might be about one swing a second Values of C1, VR1 and R3 given in Figure 3.5 provide a starting-point for experimentation. R4 should be about ten times the value of R3. The flag is waved until the reset button S2 is pressed.

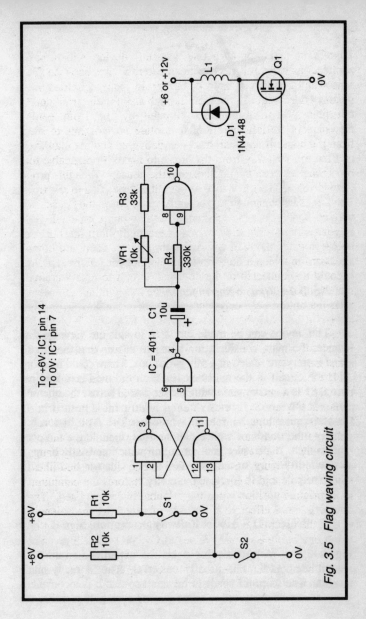

Fig. 3.5 Flag waving circuit

55

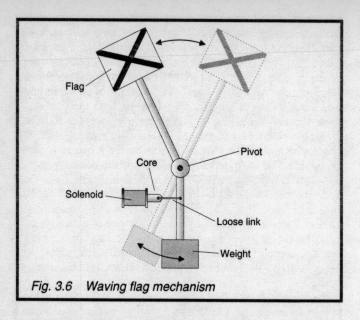

Fig. 3.6   Waving flag mechanism

The device can be made any size to suit the viewing distance, the main consideration being to ensure that the circuit and battery are sealed in a rain-proof box. There could be room for the circuit in the mail-box itself. In the mail-box application, S1 is a microswitch with a lever placed across the opening so that the switch is briefly closed when mail is pushed in. In other applications S1 can be a push-to-close push-button but many other kinds of switch can be used, including a mercury tilt-switch, a pressure mat or a magnetic reed-switch, or a circuit driven by one of the sensors of Chapter 6.   S2 will normally be a push-to-close push-button.

Project 11 – Model Railway Semaphore Signal

Although it is possible for a skilled modeller to build the complete signal, it is usually easier to adapt a ready-made signal. The solenoid needs to be small so that it is inconspicuous or can be disguised in some way or even hidden under the base-board. Small solenoids are difficult to obtain, so it is usually necessary to wind a coil for oneself. The core is a length of soft iron cut from an iron nail about 3mm in diameter. Find a piece of stiff but thin-walled plastic tube into which this core will easily slide. A length cut from the barrel of a ball-point pen is a possibility. Alternatively, wind a few turns of paper around a rod a millimetre or so greater in diameter than the core and secure the end with glue or plastic tape to prevent it from unrolling. Wind a coil of about 2000 turns of enamel-covered copper wire around the tube. The turns need not be neatly laid side by side. Use as fine a gauge wire as you can obtain, preferably 40 SWG, which is 0.125mm in diameter. The finer the gauge, the smaller the diameter of the solenoid will be. With 40 SWG wire, the coil will be about 30mm long and about 13mm in external diameter, and will have a resistance of about 100Ω. Coils of this type are not normally as powerful as commercially-made solenoids, but they are smaller and usually able to operate a light, well-balanced mechanism such as the semaphore arm.

The solenoid is mounted vertically with its core connected to the wire that raises the semaphore arm. The arm is raised when the coil is activated and is returned by gravity to its 'rest' position when the coil is de-energised. Since only small forces are involved, it is essential that the mechanism moves freely with as little friction as possible.

Project 12 – Crossing-Barrier Lifter

A solenoid may be used to raise the arm of a level-crossing barrier of a model railway. The idea of the project is very similar to that of Project 11. The solenoid is mounted vertically, possibly beneath the base-board. The core is attached to the barrier arm close to the pivot, as in the upper diagram of Figure 3.4e. When energised, it pulls down on the short arm raising the longer arm.

Chapter 4

CONTROLLING RELAYS

In essence, a relay is a solenoid-driven switch. The relay has a coil which when energised attracts a soft-iron armature toward it. The armature is shaped so as to cause one or more pairs of spring contacts to open or close. Most relay coils are rated to operate on 5V, 6V, 12V or 24V. Those operating on 5V are intended to be driven by the output of TTL logic and can also be driven by members of other logic families such as CMOS. But relays are effective over a wide range of voltages, so that most 5V and 6V types can both be operated over the range 3.5V to 12V. Most 12V types can be operated over the range 9V to 30V. It is advisable not to operate a relay for long periods on voltages at the top end of these ranges for this may lead to over-heating and possibly to burning-out of the coil.

Since relays are basically mechanical switches, they may be used to carry AC as well as DC. They are particularly useful for switching AC, for which transistor switches are not suitable. Another advantage of relays is that their contact resistance is negligible, so maximum power is available for the load. Relays are useful for switching power to electronic equipment. For example, switching on a radio set by using a transistor switch may cause problems. The characteristics of the transistor may interact with those of the radio circuits, preventing proper reception. A relay, being simply a switch as far as the radio set is concerned, allows for trouble-free control. In general, most electronic equipment such as radio sets, tape players, and even some solid-state 'buzzers' are better switched by relay. Relays also simplify the control of electric motors.

Choosing a Relay

Relays are available in a bewildering number of sizes, ratings and switching functions. Some have a single pair of contacts, normally open, which close when the coil is energised (Fig. 4.1a). Many have a pair of change-over contacts (Fig.4.1b) in which the common contact (C) touches contact B when the coil is energised, or touches A when it is not energised. The pairs of

59

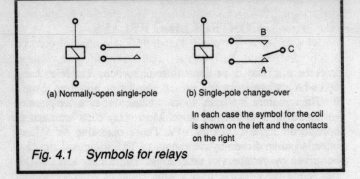

(a) Normally-open single-pole

(b) Single-pole change-over

In each case the symbol for the coil is shown on the left and the contacts on the right

Fig. 4.1   Symbols for relays

contacts are referred to as the *normally open* (NO) pair and the *normally closed* (NC) pair. Relays of this type switch one device on at the same time as they switch a second device off. Relays are also made with two and with four pairs of changeover contacts for switching a number of independent devices simultaneously.

When choosing a relay it is not only essential to have the right set of contacts and operate at the available voltage, but the rating of these contacts must considered. If the current passing through the relay is excessive this may lead to sparking as the contacts separate, particularly with inductive loads. Sooner or later the contacts will fuse together, making the relay unusable. The rating of relay contacts is roughly related to the physical size of the relay.   Relays are categorised by size as below, though the name given by one manufacturer may not entirely agree with that given by another manufacturer for a relay of similar size:

Miniature: These are the largest type that the reader is likely to use. They are, in fact, fairly large compared with most electronic components, a typical miniature relay measuring about 35mm × 20mm × 15mm. The description 'miniature' relates this type to the standard-sized relays used in industrial equipment.   Each contact-pair of a miniature relay carries currents of up to about 5A at voltages usually up to 240V AC. For exact values, see the catalogue description. Some miniature relays are chassis mountable or require special sockets. Others can be mounted directly on a pcb, but tend to take up a lot of room. Unless their ability to handle relatively large currents and voltages is required, it is preferable to choose a relay from one of the groups below.

Sub-miniature: These are intended for mounting directly on a pcb. In general, they handle smaller currents and voltages than the miniature type, but sub-miniature types able to carry up to 1A are available.

Ultra-miniature: These are the smallest type, and may often be housed in a double-in-line package of the same size as that used for integrated circuits. Even at this small size, some have up to 4 pairs of change-over contacts. Maximum currents are not usually more than 1A and may be appreciably less.

Other types of relay include:

Reed relay: this consists of two strips of springy metal sealed in a glass capsule (Fig.4.2). In a magnetic field, these strips become magnetised, are attracted toward each other and make contact, so closing the circuit. The magnetic field may be provided by a coil surrounding the relay, or by a permanent magnet brought alongside. The latter type are often used in security systems to detect if a window or door (with a permanent magnet mounted on it) is open or shut. Reed relays with coils are often enclosed in a d.i.l. package identical to that used for ics, except that there may be fewer pins. They have a relatively high coil resistance, so require only a few milliamps to drive them. However their contacts are usually rated at no more than 0.5A, though many of them can handle up to 240V

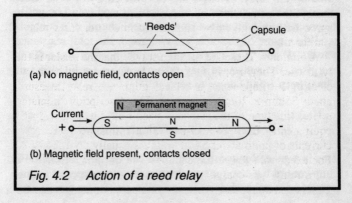

(a) No magnetic field, contacts open

(b) Magnetic field present, contacts closed

Fig. 4.2   Action of a reed relay

AC. Some include a protective diode (Fig.4.3(a)) connected across the coil.

Photomos relay: This is a type of opto-coupler including an LED and a light-activated MOSFET. It can switch DC or AC (up to 400V AC) and has a low ON resistance (as little as 0.7Ω in some types). The photomos has the advantage of silent operation (ordinary relays click!).

Controlling Relays

Much of the discussion and many of the circuits of Chapter 2 apply equally to relays. The reader is referred to the information on switches (p. 21) and to the circuits illustrated in Figures 2.1 to 2.5. Since a relay is an inductive load (excepting photomos relays), add a protective diode to the circuit as in Figure 4.3(a).

Switching by Relays

Figure 4.3 shows how to wire up a relay to perform various switching functions. At (a) is shown typical wiring for all types of relay. The protective diode may already be incorporated in the relay, in which case the coil must be connected with the correct polarity. A single-pole normally-open relay is used in Figure 4.3(b) to turn a device on when the coil is energised. In Figure 4.3(c) a double-pole changeover relay is wired as a reversing switch.

Four single-pole relays are used in Figure 4.3(d) to short-circuit one or more resistors in the chain PQ. The relay coils are energised independently of each other, and could be under the control of a 4-bit output from a logical circuit, or a computer. When none of the coils are energised, the total resistance between P and Q is 1500Ω. If one or more of the coils is energised, the resistance may take any value (in hundreds of ohms) from 1400Ω down to zero.

Project 13 – Touch-Triggered Relay

This is a general purpose circuit that can be used for ON/OFF lamp control but also for switching many other types of mains-powered device, such as a fan or a radio set. It also can be used

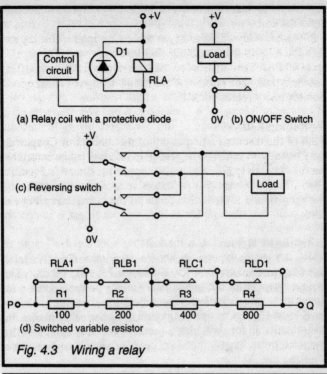

(a) Relay coil with a protective diode

(b) ON/OFF Switch

(c) Reversing switch

(d) Switched variable resistor

Fig. 4.3 Wiring a relay

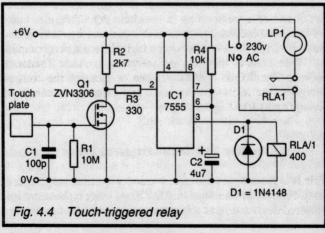

Fig. 4.4 Touch-triggered relay

D1 = 1N4148

63

as a bedside lamp, similar to Project 6, but it has the advantage that there is only a single touch-plate, which is easier to find in the dark. The touch plate can be made very large. This project controls a much brighter lamp than that in Project 6.

The touch switch is based on an n-channel MOSFET (Q1, Fig. 4.4). The resistor R1 normally pulls the gate voltage down to zero, so the transistor acts as a high resistance and the voltage at its drain terminal is almost 6V. When you touch the plate with a finger the voltage of the plate rises owing to currents induced in your body by electromagnetic fields from surrounding mains wires and mains-powered electrical equipment. This causes the MOSFET to conduct, lowering the voltage at its drain. A low voltage at the trigger input (pin 2) of the 7555 timer makes its output swing sharply high and energises the relay coil. It stays high for as long as your finger is in contact with the plate.

The timer is wired as a monostable with a pulse length of 1.1RC so, with the values shown in Figure 4.4, the relay remains switched on for $1.1 \times 10000 \times 4.7 \times 10^{-6} = 0.05$s. The lamp appears to go out immediately after you have taken your finger from the touch plate. If preferred, a higher value of resistor R4 and C2 can be used to extend the pulse. This makes the project suitable for switching a porch or corridor light. With an extended pulse length, it can be used for switching a radio set off after, say, 30 min.

If the project is to be used for switching the AC mains read the Precautions listed on pp. 38–40 before you begin to make plans. Observe the Precautions while building, testing and using the project. The project can be built into a plastic enclosure with a mains outlet socket , as in Figure 2.13. The touch plate can be any suitable metal plate; special touch-plates are available from electronics suppliers. The circuit is powered by a battery which will last a long while, since the circuit takes less than 1mA when quiescent and only 10mA when the relay is energised.

It is essential that the relay is rated for switching the current that the lamp requires. For example, if a lamp of up to 100W is to be switched, the current passing when the lamp is powered from the 230V mains is $100/230 = 0.44$A. These are rms values, which are applicable since they refer to the average power dissipated in the lamp. A miniature relay is suitable in this instance, assuming that its contacts are rated for 230V AC. There are also sub-miniature relays that are rated suitably for this application.

Project 14 – Camera Release 2

Many cameras have a remote shutter control which is actuated by closing a switch. The socket on the camera body has two contacts. Usually the socket accepts a small coaxial plug, the central conductor being positive with respect to the sheath. A relay can be used to make contact between the two, so triggering the shutter. Using a relay simply as a remote switch is of no particular advantage, as the remote control itself is a switch. But there are useful applications for a circuit that closes the relay as a result of detecting a particular event. Figure 4.5 is a circuit for triggering the camera when a beam of light is broken. This has applications in animal photography, and also in security systems for taking photographs of intruders.

Light is detected by a photodiode D1 which can be either a visible-light or infra-red diode. For security purposes an infra-red photodiode is best because the beam is invisible. When the beam is falling on D1 it produces an appreciable *leakage* current (note: it is reverse-biased) which flows through R1 and VR1, generating a potential difference across them. The potential at the (+) input of the comparator IC1 is positive, causing its output to be positive. When the beam is broken, the leakage current is sharply reduced, causing the potential at the (+) input to fall below zero. The output of the comparator falls suddenly to 0V. This falling edge triggers the timer IC3, the output of which goes high, turning on Q1 and thus energising the relay. The relay contacts close, triggering the camera shutter and the camera-flash.

The high output pulse from the timer lasts for about 0.4s which is long enough to trigger the camera but not so long that the relay remains energised, wasting current and possibly becoming overheated. This is a general design point for relay circuits. Relays require appreciable current when energised and it is preferable to design the circuit to that the relay is energised

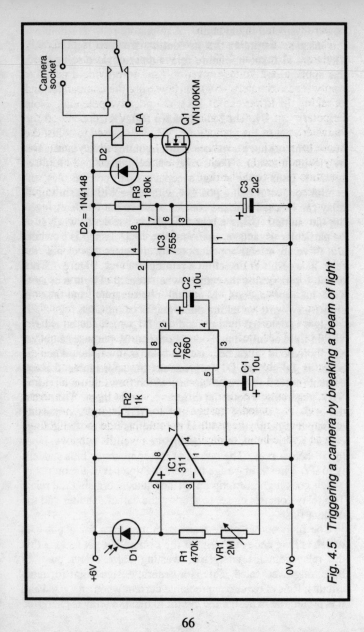

Fig. 4.5 Triggering a camera by breaking a beam of light

for periods of minimal length.

This circuit operates on a 6V supply which is preferably regulated. A regulated 5V or 12V supply could also be used. The 7660 ic is a voltage inverter, used to provide a negative supply (approximately –6V) for powering the comparator and for taking the lower end of VR1 to a negative potential. Note the polarity of C1. The values of R1 and VR1 depend on the characteristics of the photodiode, VR1 being used to adjust the circuit for working in darkness, dim light or full daylight. The relay is required to switch only a small current, so an ultra-miniature relay could be used.

Various sources of light can be used. With an infra-red sensor it is appropriate to use an infra-red source. A high-power infra-red LED such as a TIL38 is usable up to about a metre from the sensor. Power the LED from 5V or 6V, connecting it in series with a resistor (usually about 33Ω or 39Ω, 0.5W or 1W) to limit current to about 100mA. This drains a battery rather quickly so a mains power unit is preferred. This may more conveniently be separate from the unit supplying the detector circuit, and need not be regulated. Plastic lenses are available which may be used to focus the light into a beam, for greater efficiency and greater range. Another way to increase range is to wire two or more LEDs in parallel. It is also possible to use a low-power (<1mW) infra-red laser, of the type used as a lecturer's pointer. Some, but not all infra-red photodiodes are also sensitive to visible light. With these and with photodiodes responsive to visible light, any convenient source may be used. This could include room lighting, such as a table lamp, or daylight from a well-lit window.

Chapter 5

CONTROLLING MOTORS

An enormous range of motors is available but very many of them are intended for relatively heavy use in industry and will not be discussed here. The motors most commonly available and most likely to be used by model-makers, educational and similar users are low-voltage DC motors which have permanent magnets to produce the field, and the discussion will centre on these. They are inexpensive to buy and are readily available from suppliers of electronic components and from model-maker's suppliers. They can also be recovered from broken toys, car-breakers (radiator fan motors) and similar sources. We shall also touch on controlling light AC motors of the kind found in desk fans, drills, and food-mixers. Two specialist types of motor are of special interest in control systems. These are stepping motors and servo-motors, which are described later in the chapter.

Although a motor fundamentally produces rotary motion, this is easily converted into other types of motion. Figure 5.1 shows how reciprocating and linear motion may be produced by a motor. However, motors operate best at a high rate of rotation, so the rate of rotation may need reducing before the motion is converted. Gear and pulley systems can be purchased in kit form or assembled from parts found in constructional sets. Some motors have built-in gear systems. Those lacking the skills or facilities for precise engineering may often be able to devise mechanisms made from hardboard or card, and rubber bands or string, which are reminiscent of Heath Robinson in their appearance but are nevertheless satisfactory in operation. Figure 5.2 shows some examples. The mechanisms of Figure 5.2a and d rely on friction; Figure 5.1c could also be adapted to using friction instead of gearing.

Manual Control
The most common manual control for a motor is a mechanical switch. The discussion on p. 20 applies just as much to motors as it does to lamps. A variable resistor may provide speed

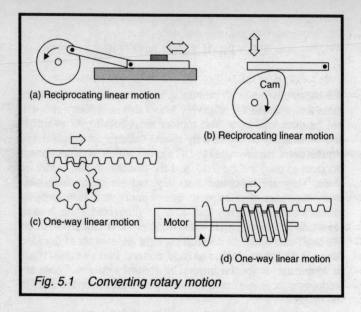

Fig. 5.1   Converting rotary motion

control for low-voltage DC motors but, for reasons of safety, a
variable resistor unit used to control the speed of mains-voltage
AC motors should be commercially built.

Solid-State Control
Transistor switches such as those shown in Figures 2.1 to 2.5
can be used for DC motors. Since motors are inductive, a protective diode (Fig.3.1) should be connected across the motor.
Transistor switches are not applicable to AC motors, even those
of low voltage, but a transistor-driven relay provides one way
of controlling AC mains motors, or those running on lower AC
voltages. Directional control of permanent magnet motors is
achieved by a relay circuit like that in Figure 4.3(c). Figure 5.3
shows directional control using MOSFET transistors. The circuit is shown operating on 6V but could also run at 12V or 15V.
The NAND gates could be replaced by a pair of NOR gates
(CMOS type 4001) or by inverting gates. The MOSFETs are
rated suitably to the current drawn by the motor. The control
voltage is set to a high or low value; it can be fed from a logic

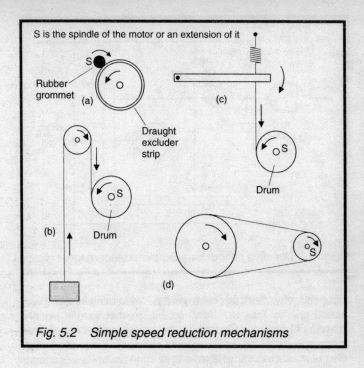

S is the spindle of the motor or an extension of it

Rubber grommet

(a)

Draught excluder strip

(b)

Drum

(c)

Drum

(d)

Fig. 5.2   Simple speed reduction mechanisms

gate output or can be switched. Switching is by a transistor switch or by a mechanical switch.

In Figure 5.4 a pair of microswitches are used to control the direction of motion of a motor-driven mechanism each time it reaches the limits of its permitted motion. In this example, a model locomotive hits a microswitch each time it reaches the end of the track, causing it to reverse, so the locomotive travels to and fro continuously. The logic of Figure 5.4 includes the inverting gates of Figure 5.3 so all the logic for the system is contained in a single 4011 ic.

For the reasons given on p. 3, solid state control of the speed of a DC motor is best achieved by a *switched-mode circuit*. One such circuit was illustrated in Figure 1.2, with a feedback version for automatic control in Figure 1.8. In Figure 5.5 the circuit of Fig 1.2 is modified by including a pair of diodes so that the charge and discharge periods of the timer ic can be set

71

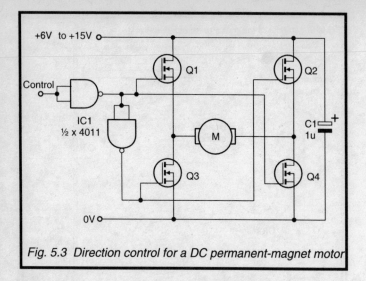

Fig. 5.3 Direction control for a DC permanent-magnet motor

independently. With this circuit is it possible to make the 'high' period shorter than the 'low' period, so that narrow widely spaced pulses are delivered to the motor, producing slower motor speeds. With the component values shown in the figure, the pulse width is variable from zero up to about 95%, giving a much wider range of speed control.

Figure 5.6 is another controller for motor speed and, like Figure 5.5, can also be used for lamp brightness control. In this circuit the 7555 is used as a clock to drive the 507C voltage-to-time ic. Speed is controlled by the voltage applied to pin 5 of IC2. In the figure, the dashed lines show a variable resistor which can be used as a manual input. But the input could also come from a sensor, perhaps one sensitive to temperature for controlling the speed of a fan. A digital-to-analogue converter under the control of a computer could also be used to provide the variable voltage input. The input voltage should normally be between 1.5V and 4.5V. The ic generates a series of 6V pulses at 1/128 of the clock rate, the pulse width being inversely proportional to the input voltage At 1.5V the output is continually high, so motor runs at full speed. As the voltage is increased, pulse width decreases and the speed is reduced. At

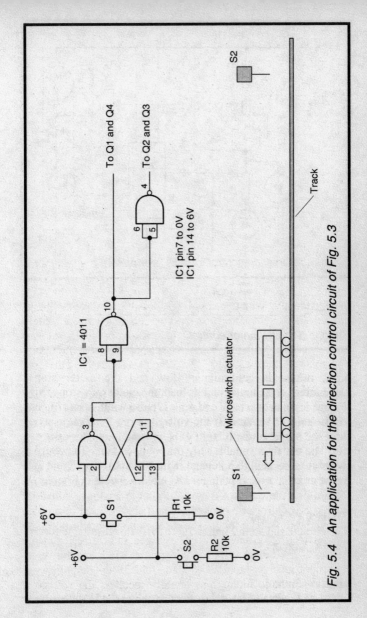

Fig. 5.4 An application for the direction control circuit of Fig. 5.3

73

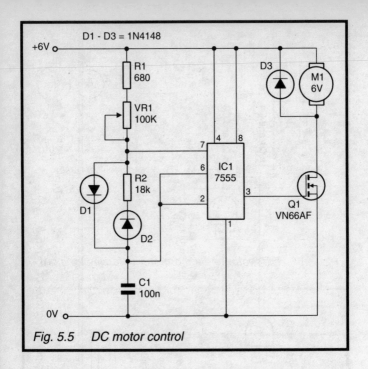

Fig. 5.5   DC motor control

4.5V, output is continuously low and the motor stops. Depending on the motor and its load, the motor may stop at any voltage input between 3V and 4.5V if pulse width is insufficient to maintain its rotation. If the voltage at pin 5 is below about 0.5V the output of the IC (pin 4) is low and the motor does not run. The circuit is suitable only for 6V operation. To control a motor running at higher voltage, wire it as shown in Figure 2.2. Some more control circuits for DC motors appear in Chapter 9.

Thyristor Control
The circuits shown in Figures 2.7 to 2.10 are all suitable for use with AC motors.

Digital Control
Ways have already been described for digital control of many

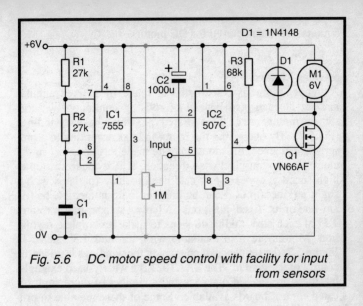

Fig. 5.6   DC motor speed control with facility for input from sensors

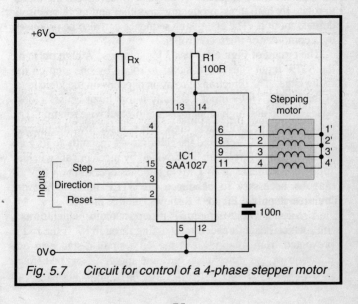

Fig. 5.7   Circuit for control of a 4-phase stepper motor

of the DC and AC control circuits described in Chapter 2. These circuits may also be used for DC motors.

Stepper Motors

A stepper motor is constructed to rotate by a fixed angular amount at each step instead of rotating continuously. Most stepper motors are of the 4-phase type, which have 4 windings (Fig.5.7). By energising the four windings according to a pre-scribed sequence, the motor may be made to step either in the clockwise or anti-clockwise direction. If it is made to step at high speed it *appears* to rotate continuously (perhaps with a slight jerkiness) but it can be brought to an immediate halt in any one of its 'fixed' positions. A typical stepper motor rotates 7.5° at each step, taking 48 steps to make a complete revolution. Motors are also available with 15° and 1.8° steps. In Figure 5.7, the sequence of energising the windings is under the control of a digital ic. The SAA1027 is a widely-used example, but there are several other ics and a number of more sophisticated control-boards available. Some of these are able to produce an extended sequence of outputs which causes the motor to rotate by half-steps, producing smoother and more precisely defined motion. The energising sequence can also be produced by a computer or microcontroller.

The circuit of Figure 5.7 has 3 logic inputs. A high pulse on the STEP input causes the motor to rotate by one step on the rising edge. The direction of rotation depends on the logic level at the DIRECTION input. Usually a low input causes clock-wise rotation and high input causes anti-clockwise rotation. The reset input is normally held high. If it is made low, the internal counter is reset to zero and the rotor moves instantly to its zero position. Input levels can be provided by mechanical switches, solid-state switches or by CMOS logic ics operating on 12V. It may be necessary to debounce the STEP input to prevent multiple stepping. Figure 5.8 shows suitable circuits.

A *stepping linear actuator* is a stepper motor which turns a 'nut' which has a threaded rod passing through it. If the rod is prevented from rotating, it is moved a small distance in one direction or the other each time the motor is stepped. Such devices are relatively expensive but have applications where

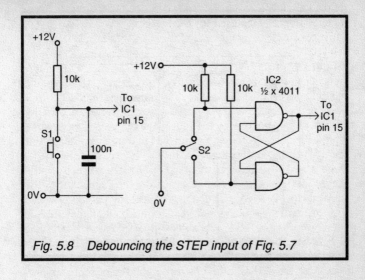

Fig. 5.8   Debouncing the STEP input of Fig. 5.7

precisely controlled linear positioning over a relatively short distance is required.

Project 15 – Automatic Curtain Drawing

The exact mechanical details of this project depend on the type, size and weight of the curtains, the type of curtain railway and the nature of the window or doorway. Figure 5.9 shows the basic principle of a motorised curtain railway. The edge of the curtain is attached to an endless loop of cord, which is held under light tension by a spring or elastic cord. The cord is wound once or twice around a narrow cylinder which is turned by the motor. The narrowness of the cylinder provides the gearing-down of the motor. Some experimentation is required to find the right tension, the right type of cord and a suitable motor. Two microswitches are located so that they detect whether the curtain is open or closed. The cord passes through a hole in the lever of each microswitch, or in some other way it is arranged that one microswitch (S2) is closed when the curtain is fully open and the other one (S3) is closed when the

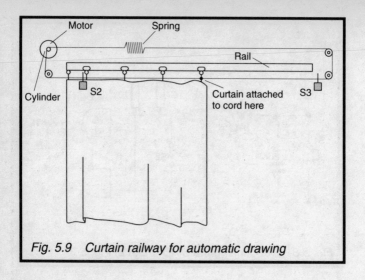

Fig. 5.9 Curtain railway for automatic drawing

curtain is fully closed.

The circuit is shown in Figure 5.10, which links to the motor-reversing circuit of Figure 5.3. Assume that we start with the curtain open, so that S2 was the switch most recently closed, the reversing flip-flop is set and the control output to Figure 5.3 is high. If the motor was powered, this would make the motor turn in the direction required to close the curtain. Nothing happens to start with as the ON/OFF flip-flop is reset and no power is supplied to the reversing circuit. Pressing S1 sets the ON/OFF flip-flop which turns on Q1 and energises the relay. This closes and supplies power to the motor reversing circuit (Fig.5.3). The motor turns on and gradually closes the curtain. When the curtain is fully closed, S3 closes and the ON/OFF flip-flop is reset. The change of output of the ON/OFF flip-flop is detected by the circuitry in the centre of Figure 5.10. This combination of a delay, an exclusive-OR gate (conveniently built from four NAND gates) and an invert gate (also from NAND) normally delivers a high output to the ON-OFF flip-flop. Whenever it detects a change of input from the reversing gate, it produces a short low pulse. This resets the ON/OFF flip-flop and the motor is turned off.

78

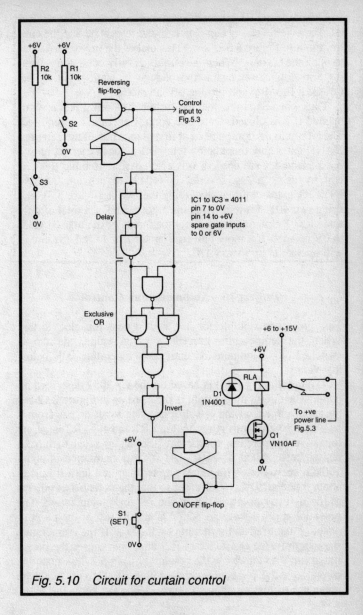

Fig. 5.10   Circuit for curtain control

79

The next time S1 is pressed, the motor starts as before. But this time the reversing flip-flop is in the reset state and the control input to Figure 5.3 is low. This makes the motor turn so as to open the curtain. When the curtain is fully open, the reversing flip-flop is set again, the change in state resetting the ON/OFF flip-flop and turning off the motor.

Thus when S1 is pressed, the curtain is closed if it is open or opened if it is closed. Only one control operation is required. The circuit looks complicated at first glance but all the gates are NAND gates and, there being four such gates in each ic, only 4 inexpensive ics are needed. It is also possible to build this circuit by using a hex inverter ic (4049) to provide the five INVERT gates required (including the two in Figure 5.3), and using two 4011 ics to provide the eight NANDs, a total of only three ics. Remember to connect the inputs of the unused gates to 0V or +6V. If a more powerful motor is required, the circuit will operate at up to 15V DC.

Project 16 – Automatic Fan Control

This project is suitable for use with a desk-top electric fan. When the temperature exceeds a given value, the fan is switched on. It remains on until the temperature falls below that value.

The circuit (Fig.5.11) is based on the CA3059 described on p. 32. The circuit on the right is the same as in Figure 2.12 but the input circuit on the left differs. The input comes from a potential divider consisting of R1, VR1 and R2. R2 is an ntc (negative temperature coefficient) thermistor rated to have a resistance of 47kΩ at 25°C. At 0°C its resistance is about 100kΩ, decreasing with increasing temperature until it falls to about 37kΩ at 30°C. VR1 is set so that the potential at pin 9 is at the halfway point, 3.25V at the required temperature. The potential at pin 13 is also 3.25V. The ic is just at the point of enabling the triac and switching on the fan. If the temperature rises slightly, the resistance of R2 falls. This causes the potential at pin 9 to fall. Now the potential of pin 9 is less than that of pin 13 and the ic begins sending pulses to Q1. Q1 begins to conduct and the fan begins to turn. If the fan cools the room,

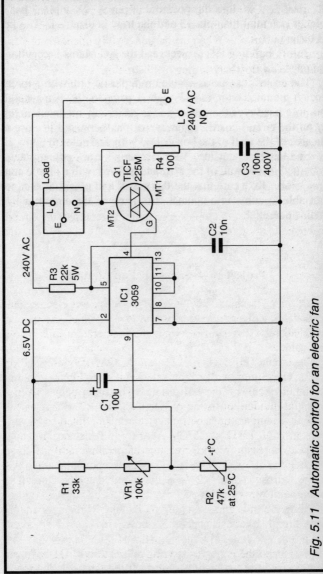

Fig. 5.11 Automatic control for an electric fan

or if the room is cooled for some other reason, the resistance of R2 rises and so does the potential at pin 9. Now pin 9 has a higher potential than pin 13 and the triac is disabled. The fan is turned off.

Before building this project read the AC Mains Precautions on pages 38 to 40.

The project can be assembled in a plastic box with a mains socket mounted on it, as in Project 5, page 36. R2 is a general-purpose bead type thermistor and is preferably mounted directly on the circuit board. Arrange that the thermistor is close to an area of the wall of the box drilled with fine holes to allow air to circulate from outside. VR1 is a cermet track potentiometer mounted on the wall of the box, and is fitted with a plastic control knob. Take care that the thermistor and potentiometer are not able to come into contact with parts of the circuit at live mains potential.

Chapter 6

SIGNAL PROCESSING

Chapters 2 to 5 have described examples of the controlled elements commonly found in control systems. In the simplest systems there is a direct link between the input device, such as a switch and the controlled element, such as a motor. In more complicated systems the link between input and output comprises one or more stages in which the signal from the input is processed on its way to the controlled element. There may also be a feedback signal to be processed. The four most common processing operations are amplifying, comparing, triggering and conversion. The term 'conversion' includes the conversion of analogue signals to digital form and the conversion of digital signals to analogue form.

Amplifiers

The signal from a sensor (see Chapters 7 and 8) may be too small to be used directly for driving the controlled element. It needs to be amplified. Transistor amplifiers are frequently used but the most practicable kind of amplifier in control circuits is the *operational amplifier*, or *op amp*. Op amps are available as integrated circuits and there is an extremely wide range of them with different characteristics. They have very high gain (the open-loop gain) which is normally not made full use of. Instead, we limit the gain by using a feedback resistor which allows the gain to be fixed very precisely. Op amps operate on a split power supply, such as ±6V or ±15V, but some are capable of working on low supply voltages, such as ±1V. Some are able to work on a single supply. All op amps have two inputs, the inverting input (−) and the non-inverting input (+), and have a single output. Figure 6.1 shows the pinout which is common to almost all ics which contain just one amplifier. Pins that are unmarked in Figure 6.1 may have no connections or may be used for special purposes, depending on the type of op amp. Ics containing 2 or 4 op amps are also available.

Op amps are divided into groups depending on their input characteristics. Bipolar op amps, with BJTs at their inputs,

83

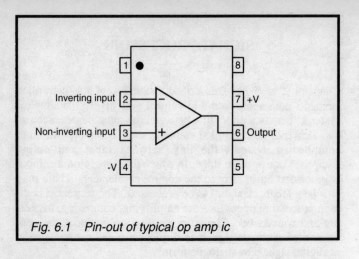

Fig. 6.1   Pin-out of typical op amp ic

include many cheap, general-purpose devices. An example is the widely used 741 ic. JFET op amps have junction FETs at their inputs, and consequently have very high input impedance. The TL081 is a general-purpose op amp in this class and has low supply voltage (minimum, ±2V), which makes it useful for battery-powered equipment. CMOS op amps, such as the CA3140, have extremely high input impedance, and can operate on ±2V. Another CMOS op amp is the ICL7611 which operates on ±1V and has the advantage that its output can swing up to +V and down to –V. Its performance is programmable by connecting pin 8 to +V (supply current = 10μA), 0V (supply current 100μA) or –V (supply current = 1mA). The bandwidth of the op amp increases with increasing supply current.

Figure 6.2 shows an op amp in an inverting amplifier circuit. Note the two power supply terminals. The feedback resistor is R_F. The gain of this circuit is given by:

$$V_{OUT} = V_{IN} \times -R_F/R_A$$

R_B can be omitted but, for best results, make R_B equal to the values of R_A and R_F in parallel. This equation has some limitations. V_{IN} must not be greater than the positive supply (+V) or less than the negative supply (–V). In all types of op amp, the

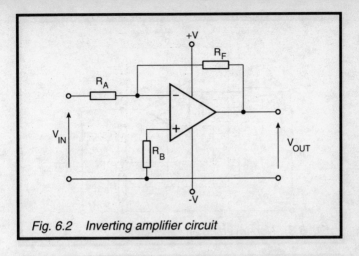

Fig. 6.2   Inverting amplifier circuit

output voltage can not be greater than +V or less than –V. In many types, the maximum output voltage is 1 or 2 volts less than +V and the minimum is 1 or 2 volts greater than –V. Limitations of this kind apply to all op amp circuits. Although the input impedance of the op amps is very high (usually 2MΩ) in most bipolar types and much higher (up to $10^{12}\Omega$) in JFET and CMOS op amps, this is the input impedance *of the op amp itself*. The input impedance of the *amplifier circuit* may be much less than this. In Figure 6.2, the potential at the (–) input is always 0V so that it acts as a ground. Consequently the input impedance *of the circuit* equals R_A.

A *non-inverting amplifier* is shown in Figure 6.3. This has the advantage of very high input impedance since the input is connected only to the (+) input of the op amp. The gain of this circuit is given by:

$$V_{OUT} = V_{IN} \times (R_A + R_F)/R_A$$

R_B can be omitted but, for best results, make R_B equal to the values of R_A and R_F in parallel. A variation of Figure 6.3 is shown in Figure 6.4. In effect, this circuit makes R_F equal to zero and R_A equal to infinity. In the equation above we find that, as resistors approach these values, the equation simplifies to:

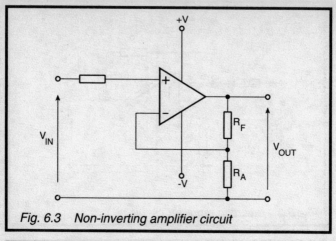

Fig. 6.3   Non-inverting amplifier circuit

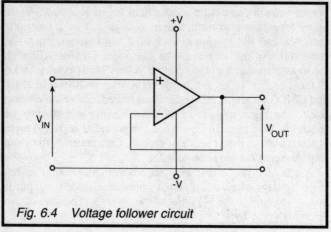

Fig. 6.4   Voltage follower circuit

$$V_{OUT} = V_{IN}$$

This circuit is known as a *voltage follower*. Its main use in control systems is when a sensor circuit is unable to supply sufficient current to drive a subsequent circuit, such as a transistor switch. The voltage follower circuit requires virtually no input current, but its maximum output current is that of the op

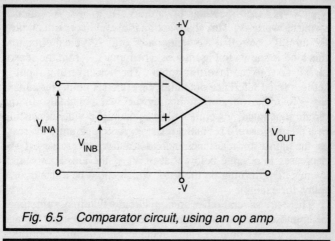

Fig. 6.5   Comparator circuit, using an op amp

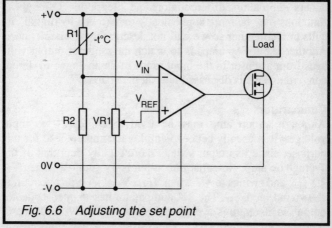

Fig. 6.6   Adjusting the set point

amp, which may be as high as 50mA, or even more in the case of a power op amp.

The circuit of Figure 6.5 has two high-impedance inputs. It has no feedback and makes use of the very high open-loop gain of the op amp. The output voltage is proportional to V_{INB} – V_{INA} but, unless the difference between them is exceedingly small, the output swings as far as it can go toward +V or –V. If

87

$V_{INB} > V_{INA}$ then it swings toward $+V$. If $V_{INB} < V_{INA}$ then it swings toward $-V$. This sharp action is useful in control circuits for turning controlled elements on or off. A typical circuit of this kind is shown in Figure 6.6. The input V_{IN} from the sensor circuit goes to the inverting input. The non-inverting input is set to a fixed reference potential V_{REF} (the set point) by adjusting VR1. The op amp compares the two potentials. In the circuit illustrated, V_{IN} comes from a potential divider consisting of a thermistor (p. 111) and a resistor. As temperature decreases, the thermistor resistance increases and V_{IN} decreases. If V_{IN} decreases to a value below that of V_{REF}, the amplifier output swings high, turning on the load, which could be a heater or a relay, for example.

There are several other op amp circuits that may sometimes be employed in control circuits to detect when an input voltage reaches the set point. These include logarithmic amplifiers, adders, subtractors, differentiators and integrators. Often these functions may be more conveniently undertaken by digital circuits or a computer so we will not describe these circuits here. Another use for op amps is to match the range of output voltages from a sensor to the input range of an analogue-to-digital converter. This is discussed later in the chapter.

Comparators
Although an op amp may be used to compare two input voltages, it is usually better to employ a comparator ic for this purpose, since its output swings more rapidly than that of the average op amp. Note that the output is 0V (not $-V$) when $V_{IN} < V_{REF}$, and swings to $+V$ when $V_{IN} > V_{REF}$. A typical circuit is shown in Figure 6.7. The 311 comparator has an open-collector output so it requires a pull-up resistor, typically $1k\Omega$, represented by R1 in Figure 6.7. The resistor is shown connected to $+V$ but it can be connected to a higher voltage if a greater upward output swing is required.

Trigger Circuits
Suppose that the circuit of Figure 6.6 is adapted by substituting a light-dependent resistor (p. 109) for the thermistor, and the load is a lamp. The circuit now functions as a lamp controller, switching on the lamp as the level of illumination falls.

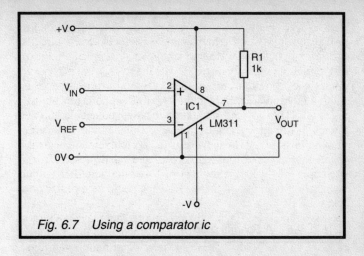

Fig. 6.7   Using a comparator ic

Incidentally, this is just one more example of how many of the basic circuits in this book can so easily be modified to perform an entirely different function. In darkness, the resistance of the LDR increases, making V_{IN} fall below V_{REF}. This causes the output to rise, turning on the lamp.

This circuit is practicable as a heater controller but as a lamp controller it has a serious disadvantage. V_{IN} falls slowly at dusk and the effects of clouds passing over the sun or of the long evening shadows may cause light levels to fall irregularly. The overall fall may be masked at times by short-term rises. The effect is that the lamp flickers on and off at dusk in an irritating way.

This effect is virtually eliminated by using positive feedback in the circuit, as in Figure 6.8. This is easily done by adding just one resistor, R_F. At dusk, V_{IN} falls until it becomes less than V_{REF} and the output swings high, switching on the lamp. The effect of the high output is fed back through R_F to the (+) input of the comparator, pulling it higher than the original value V_{REF}. From now on, if V_{IN} increases by a small amount, it will not rise high enough to exceed the potential at the (+) input. The output stays high. Only if V_{IN} increases by a large amount, sufficient to overcome the effect of the feedback, is it possible for the output to become low again. After that has happened, the potential

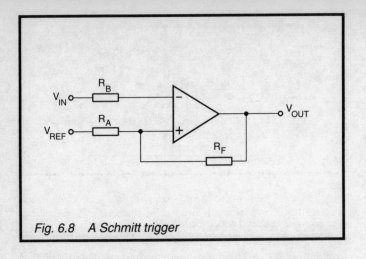

Fig. 6.8   A Schmitt trigger

at (+) is pulled lower than V_{REF}. From now on, the output can not be changed by small decreases of V_{IN}. Only a large decrease can have any effect. The result is a circuit which has hysteresis, and is known as a Schmitt trigger. At the changeover (or threshold) points its output swings very sharply with a small change in input and, once the circuit has been triggered, it takes a large reversal of the input change to reverse the output state. The threshold input voltages at which the output changes state depend on the values chosen for R_A and R_F. R_B is equal to the values of R_A and R_F in parallel. Assuming the output switches to +V or –V, the threshold levels V_T are:

$$V_T = \pm V \times R_F/(R_A + R_F)$$

Values of 100kΩ and 10kΩ are typical for R_F and R_A, respectively.

Schmitt triggers may be built either from op amps or comparators. They may also be made from a CMOS buffer gate, as in Figure 6.9. The buffer gate may be replaced by two invert gates in cascade.

Analogue-to-Digital Conversion

There are many analogue-to-digital ics available, suited to a

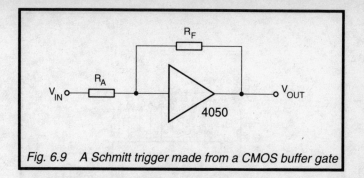

Fig. 6.9   A Schmitt trigger made from a CMOS buffer gate

wide range of purposes but for general use in a control circuit context, the ZN427E has many useful features. It is an 8-bit converter, which is adequate for most control applications, and has a maximum conversion time of 15μs. It has 3-state outputs (see below) so that several converters can be enabled, one at a time, to feed data to a single data bus. This makes it suitable for interfacing to the input port of a computer or to a micro-controller.

A circuit for the ZN427E is shown in Figure 6.10. Note that the supply voltage must be between 4.5V and 5.5V. It also requires a negative supply to provide a current I_{EXT} between 25μA and 150μA. With the 82kΩ resistor shown in Figure 6.10, a negative supply of –5V is suitable and this can be provided from a 7660 voltage inverter, as shown. The inverter could be used to provide a supply for other converters or for op amps if the total demand is not too high. Otherwise, omit the inverter and use a battery or negative power supply unit supplying –3V to –30V, selecting the value of R5 to provide a negative supply current within the required range. The converter is driven by a clock, the 7555 ic in Figure 6.10, running at up to 900kHz for the fastest conversion rate. Here we run it at 100kHz, which gives a conversion time of 90μs.

The circuit has three inputs. V_{IN} is the analogue voltage to be converted. This must be in the range 0V to 2.5V. An op amp can be used to adjust the input signal to the correct range, as explained later in the chapter. START is normally high and a low pulse to this input causes conversion of the present input voltage to begin. The OUTPUT ENABLE input controls the 3-

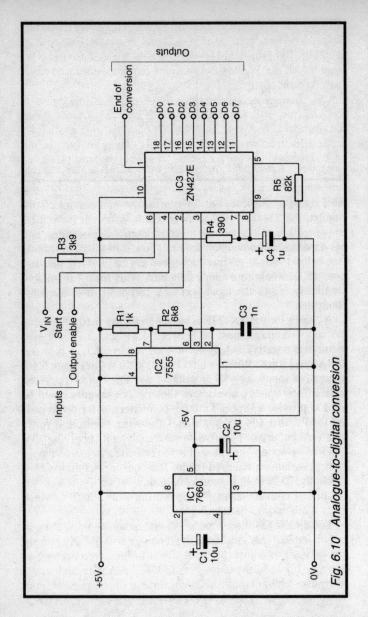

Fig. 6.10 Analogue-to-digital conversion

state outputs. When this input is low, the outputs are in the high impedance state and no digital signal is obtainable from the outputs. When OUTPUT ENABLE is high, the outputs are enabled. If the 3-state function is not required, this input can be wired permanently to +5V.

As soon as a conversion is initiated by a low pulse on START, the END OF CONVERSION output goes low. When conversion is complete, the EOC output goes high again, indicating that the converted digital data is then present at the output. The eight bits are numbered from D0, the least significant bit, to D7 the most significant bit. As the analogue input voltage ranges from 0V to 2.5V, the output ranges from 0000 0000 to 1111 1111. Output has 256 possible values, so a single step in the output corresponds to $2.5/256 = 9.76$mV.

The 507C voltage to time converter, described on p. 72 is also suitable for analogue to digital conversion. Its output is a train of pulses the width of which is proportional to the input voltage. Measuring voltage thus becomes a matter of measuring time. The output is fed to a computer or microcontroller programmed to read its value every few microseconds. The length of the pulses can then be established.

Digital-to-Analogue Conversion

Figure 6.11 shows a circuit for the ZN428E digital-to-analogue converter. Like the ZN427E, it requires a power supply between 4.5V and 5.5V. It has eight digital inputs numbered from D_0 (least significant bit) to D_7 (most significant bit). The only control input is the ENABLE input. When this is low, input data is passed straight through for conversion, which takes about 800ns. The output follows changes in the input. When ENABLE is made high the data is latched and the output voltage is fixed until ENABLE goes low again. This allows rapidly changing digital data to be sampled at a given instant.

This ic incorporates its own reference voltage of 2.55V. Since the digital input covers the range 0000 0000 to 1111 1111 (0 to 225), the output increases by 10mV for each upward step in the digital input.

Scale and Offset

We often need to feed the output from a sensor circuit to an

93

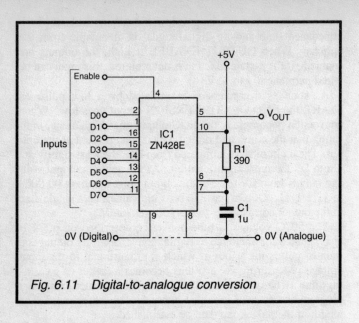

Fig. 6.11   Digital-to-analogue conversion

analogue-to-digital converter but it is seldom that this can be done directly. For example, suppose that the output of the sensor ranges from 0V to 0.1V over the range of interest. If fed to a ZN427E A-to-D converter, the output of the converter increases by 1 for every increase of 9.76mV from the sensor. The converter reads 100/9.76 = 10 when input is 0.1V so the output varies from 0000 0000 to only 0000 1010 over the whole output range of the sensor. The four most significant bits of the conversion are always 0. To put it another way, the output has a resolution of 1 in 10 steps, or 10% precision. For higher precision we need to amplify the output of the sensor to make it span much more of the input range of the converter. Amplifying by 25 increases its range maximum to 2.5V, giving a converted output ranging from 0 to 250 with 0.4% precision. A single op amp connected as a *non-inverting amplifier* (Fig. 6.3) performs the scaling. Given the equation on p. 85 and representing the gain V_{OUT}/V_{IN}, by A, the equation becomes:

94

$$R_F = R_A(A - 1)$$

In this example the gain is 25 and a suitable value for R_A is 10kΩ. Now calculate:

$$R_F = 10kΩ \times 24 = 240kΩ$$

Wire a variable resistor in the feedback loop in series with R_F, to allow the amplification to be trimmed to the required value. In this example, a fixed resistor of 220kΩ in series with a 4.7kΩ preset resistor provide the right amount of trimming.

Another problem that often arises is that the useful output range of a sensor may not begin at zero. For example, the output may range from 0.2V to 0.7V. Here the output spans 0.5V but it is offset from zero by 0.2V. It is preferable to adjust for offset after amplifying the value since we can compensate for offset errors in the amplifiers themselves at the same time as we adjust for the offset of the values. The circuit is shown in Figure 6.12, and may be adapted in various ways to suit different situations. The first stage is to adjust the scale to fit the 2.5V range of the A-to-D converter; we need to amplify by 5. In this circuit we use an *inverting* amplifier since the value is re-inverted at the second stage. Given $A = 5$ and the value of the input resistor (previously referred to as R_A) is 10kΩ, the required value of R_{FI} is $A \times R_A = 50kΩ$. This could be met by making $R2 = 47kΩ$ and $VR1 = 10kΩ$.

As the input to the first amplifier varies from 0.2V to 0.7V, its output varies from −1V to −3.5V. We assume that the power supply to the amplifier is sufficient to allow its output to swing to −3.5V. A ±5V supply will normally be suitable. To make the offset adjustment we need to add 1V to the output, so that it swings from 0V to −2.5V, then pass it through an inverting amplifier with a gain of −1, so that it swings from 0V to +2.5V. The offset adjustment is made by feeding an additional current to the inverting input of an op amp wired as an inverting amplifier. The additional current comes from the potential-divider VR2 through R4. An op amp has the property that all *currents* flowing to the inverting input are added together so that, if R3 = R4 as shown here, we can in effect add the *voltages* giving rise to these currents. One of these voltages is the output from

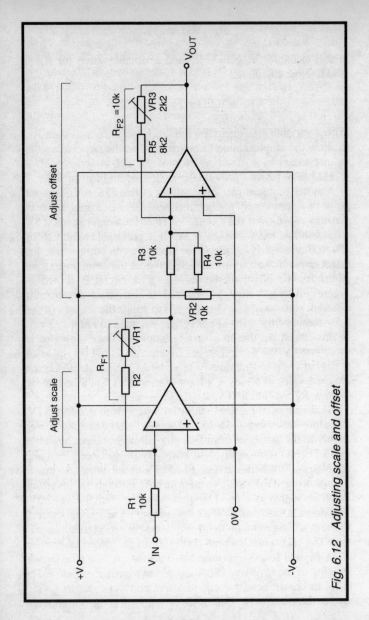

Fig. 6.12 Adjusting scale and offset

the scaling amplifier. The other is the voltage at the wiper of VR2. If this is set to +1V, the effective input to the offset amplifier ranges from 0V to –2.5V. R_{F2} equals the two input resistors R3 and R4 (both 10kΩ) so the gain of the amplifier is –1. The output ranges from 0 to 2.5V and so is matched to the analogue-to-digital converter. In practice, by adjusting VR1 carefully, the overall gain may be raised to 2.55, covering the whole input range of the converter.

Project 17 – Thermometer With Digital Output

This thermometer measures temperature to the nearest degree over the range 0° to 25° and has an 8-bit output suitable for interfacing to a computer. It is easy to adapt the project to operate over smaller or larger ranges between –40°C and 110°C. It has applications in data logging outdoor or room temperatures and also as a sensor for automatic computer-based or micro-controller-based control systems, particularly in process control.

Temperature is measured by a band-gap thermal sensor, connected as in Figure 8.5, with a ±5V supply. The –5V supply is obtained from a 7660 wired as a voltage inverter (see IC1, Fig.6.10). Over the temperature range 0°C to 25°C the output of the sensor varies from 0V to 0.025V. The output is fed to a non-inverting amplifier (Fig.6.3) with a gain of 100 to scale the output from 0V to 2V (see p. 95). This too has a ±5V supply, the negative supply being obtained from a 7660 voltage inverter. There is no need for offset adjustment. Finally, the voltage from the scaling amplifier is fed to a ZN427E analogue to digital converter, wired as in Figure 6.10. The A-to-D converter is interfaced to a computer or microcontroller, as described on page 166. The computer reads in the temperature as a binary value in the range 0 to 200, each step corresponding to a temperature difference of 0.5°C. There is no point in reading more precisely than this as the bandgap sensor has an accuracy of ±0.4°C over much of its range.

Chapter 7

MECHANICAL SENSORS

In this and the next chapter we consider some of the many devices that can be used to input data to a control system. This chapter deals with devices concerned with information that is considered to be mechanical – position, angular position, and force. Chapter 8 deals with sensors of non-mechanical physical quantities such as light, heat and magnetic field strength. In many books, devices of these kinds are referred to as *transducers*. Formally, a transducer is a device which converts one form *of energy* to another form *of energy*. It follows from this definition that rubbing two sticks together to light a fire is an example of transduction. By contrast, a sensor is a device the output of which is related to some physical quantity. Position is not a form of energy, so a device which senses the position of an object is not a transducer. Neither is a thermistor (p. 111) which senses temperature by a change in its resistance, since resistance is not a form of energy. But thermocouples and piezo-electric crystals are energy-converters, so they are transducers as well as being sensors.

Position Sensors

In a sense, an ordinary toggle switch is a mechanical sensor, for its output depends on the position to which the toggle lever has been moved. Certainly, microswitches are very useful as position sensors. In Figure 5.4, for example, a pair of microswitches is used to determine the position of the locomotive. Used in this way, each switch is known as a *limit switch*, which tells us whether or not the locomotive has reached the ends of the track. Similarly in Figure 5.9, each microswitch supplies information on the position of the curtain. Microswitches have many applications as position sensors in control systems and supply useful feedback information. A motor is switched on to propel the locomotive or draw a curtain; a microswitch tells the circuit when the task has been completed. Position sensing is very important in sequential control systems (p. 194).

A magnetic reed switch (p. 61) is another device for position detection. In security systems a reed switch is mounted on the frame of a door or window and a magnet on the door or window itself. When the door or window is open, the reed switch is open. When the door or window is closed the magnet is brought close to the reed switch, causing the switch to close. In most security systems, opening the door or window opens the switch and triggers the alarm circuits. Reed switches have other many other applications. A magnet is mounted on a part of a machine so that it comes close to the reed switch under certain circumstances. For example, the magnet might be on a safety gate to detect if the gate is fully closed. In a model railway, a magnet is mounted on the underside of the locomotive or one of the rolling stock. A reed switch is placed between the rails. The switch closes for an instant while the locomotive or rolling stock passes by, informing the system that the train has entered or left a given section of the line.

Magnetic fields can be detected by Hall effect sensors (p.114). Some kinds of Hall effect sensor have switched outputs and are useful as position sensors.

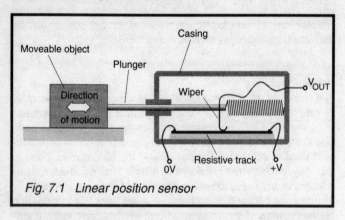

Fig. 7.1   Linear position sensor

Switches inform the system whether a given object is or is not at its expected position. It may sometimes be necessary to determine the precise position of an object within a given range. One way of doing this is to use a *linear position sensor* (Fig.7.1). As the object (which might be a cradle carrying a workpiece) moves from left to right, the plunger is forced further into the casing of the unit and the wiper of the resistor moves along the track. The potential at the wiper is dependent on the position of the object. The device acts as a potential divider and V_{OUT} increases as the object moves toward the right. The wiper is connected to a circuit which measures this potential and, from this, calculates the position of the object. By measuring the position at regular intervals of time, the velocity of the object can be calculated. In an analogue system the rate of change of position (velocity) could be calculated by an op amp differentiator circuit. In a digital system the calculation would be done by a program. The principle of the position sensor is extended to the measurement of acceleration. In Figure 7.2 the mass compresses the spring when the device is accelerated. The greater the acceleration, the greater the compression. The position of the mass is determined by using a linear position sensor, as above. Using a linear potentiometer, such as is commonly found in audio equipment, it is often possible to make use of the principle of the linear position sensor when building home-made position-sensing devices.

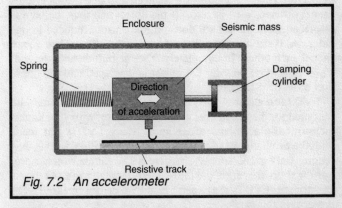

Fig. 7.2 An accelerometer

An LVDT, or *linear variable differential transformer* (Fig.7.3) is a precise way of detecting position and does not suffer from the disadvantages of track wear and consequent non-linearity of the method described above. It is one of the most widely-used devices in control systems. The alternating

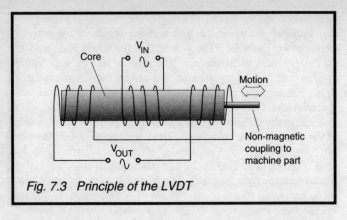

Fig. 7.3 Principle of the LVDT

current passing through the central coil generates an alternating magnetic field. The two outer coils are magnetically linked to the central coil by a ferromagnetic core. This core is attached to the object the position of which is to be sensed. When the object is at the centre of its reach, the core is centrally situated between the two outer coils and equal but opposite currents are induced in each. The coils are connected to that these currents cancel out and V_{OUT} is zero. If the object and thus the core is displaced from the central position, the current induced in one outer coil is stronger than that induced in the other. They do not cancel each other out completely. The magnitude and phase of V_{OUT} depend on how far the object is displaced and the direction of its displacement.

LVDTs measure only small displacements. Some are designed for displacements as small as ±1mm, while the largest measure displacements of ±50mm. Many LVDTs are made with the oscillator and demodulator circuits built in, so that they require only a DC supply and give a DC output voltage proportional to the core position. Unfortunately for the home constructor, LVDTs are expensive, so we do not feature LVDT projects in this book.

Optical position sensors are relatively easy to build tailormade for a given application. The principle of the simplest form is shown in Figure 7.4. A transparent strip with opaque bars is attached to the moving part. It is has low mass and produces virtually no friction, so its presence exerts minimum

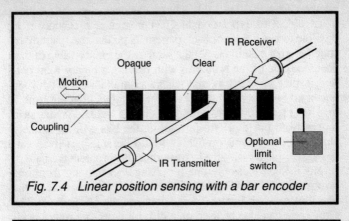

Fig. 7.4 Linear position sensing with a bar encoder

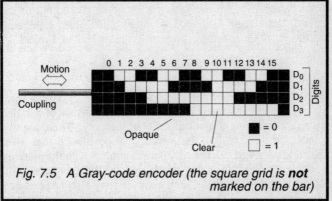

*Fig. 7.5 A Gray-code encoder (the square grid is **not** marked on the bar)*

interference with the machine to which it is attached. As the strip moves it alternately breaks and re-makes the beam of light from the IR source. The output from the IR sensor is a series of pulses, perhaps slow ones, which are counted by a digital counter, or by a computer. By keeping count of the pulses, the position of the moving part is known.

The principle of Figure 7.4 can be adapted to rotary motion by using a transparent disc bearing radiating opaque bars. The bar-counting method is suitable only for motion in one direction. An improved technique is shown in Figure 7.5. The strip is patterned with opaque areas to represent the 4-bit binary

103

numbers from 0000 to 1111. Thus it can determine the position of an object to 1 position in 16. For greater precision, it is possible to use a 6-bit or 8-bit pattern. Note that the 'pattern' or code for each position is not the same as the binary value of that position. One of the problems with reading a binary 4-bit pattern is that several bits may change simultaneously between one binary number and the next. For example, in going from 7 to 8 (0111 to 1000) all four bits change value. As the strip moves from position 7 to position 8, the bits will most likely change one at a time, producing four different short-lived values during the transition. To overcome this problem the pattern of bits is such that only one bit changes in moving from one position to the next. There are several possible sequences, the one illustrated in Figure 7.5 is known as the *Gray code*. The Gray code can also be used on a disc for detecting rotary positions. Special ics are available for decoding the output of the circuit, converting Gray-coded values into binary-numbered positions. A Gray-code converter is described in Project 19 below.

Attitude Sensors

The attitude of a machine-part with respect to gravity is most simply detected by using a *tilt-switch*. This consists of a sealed capsule containing a small quantity of mercury. There are two contacts projecting into the mercury, so positioned that when the capsule is vertical, they are both in contact with the mercury and there is conduction through the switch. If the capsule is tilted the contact is broken. Such a switch may also be used as a vibration-detector. There are many other ways in which attitude may be sensed. Figure 7.6a shows how to make a tilt detector and Figure 7.6b shows a device which has an output voltage proportional to the amount of tilt.

Force Sensors

The most commonly used sensor for relatively large forces is the *strain gauge*. This consists of a thin foil (usually metal) of complex shape mounted on a thin plastic film and cemented to a metallic structure (usually steel or aluminium). When the structure is distorted by force, the strain gauge distorts too. This causes its resistance to change slightly, in proportion to the

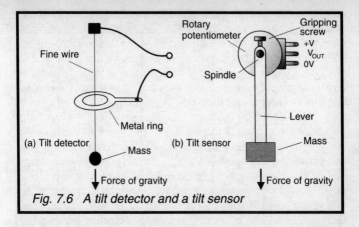

Fig. 7.6 A tilt detector and a tilt sensor

force applied. The small change in resistance is usually measured by wiring the strain gauge into a Wheatstone bridge, a circuit which is sensitive to small changes. As well as measuring the distortion of structures such as pylons and cranes, the strain gauge is used to measure compression, tension and weight. Strain gauges are also made from semiconducting materials, and this type is general more sensitive.

Smaller forces are detectable by a narrow cylinder of specially-prepared piezo-ceramic material a few millimetres long, known as a *bi-morph* element. Its action is similar to that of a crystal microphone. When the element is stressed or vibrated an electrical signal is generated. Piezo-cable has similar properties and uses, being sensitive to vibration, stress and pressure.

Project 18 – Bar Encoder

This is a linear position sensor adaptable to a wide range of applications and based on Figure 7.4. The IR transmitter and receiver diodes are of the miniature type suited for operating at a range of a few millimetres. They are mounted on the circuit board with their leads bent so that they are directed at each other with about 5mm between them. The encoder strip passes between them. The optical part of this device must be shielded

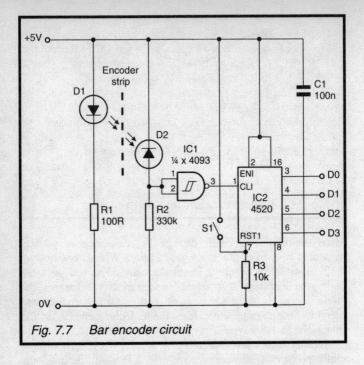

Fig. 7.7   Bar encoder circuit

from external light, though it will work unshielded in dim artificial light.

The circuit in Figure 7.7 has a 5V supply so that it may be interfaced to a computer. If it is not intended to interface it, the power supply can be 6V. When a clear area of the encoder is between D1 and D2, a strong leakage current passes through D2 and creates a potential difference across R2. This causes the voltage at the input of the NAND gate to rise to about 5.3V (this is greater than 5V because of the forward voltage drop of the diode). This high input to the gate causes its output to go low. This has no effect on the counter. When an opaque area comes between D1 and D2, the leakage current is much reduced and the input to the NAND gate falls to about 1V. This is taken as a low input, the output of the gate goes high and the counter is advanced by one step. Note that this circuit uses a NAND gate with Schmitt trigger (p. 90) input. This is to avoid multiple triggering of the counter if the encoder moves slowly.

The figure shows only one gate out of the four present in 4093 and only one of the two counters in the 4520. Remember to tie all unused inputs to 0V or 5V. Unused inputs are pins 5, 6, 8, 9, 11, 12 in IC1 and pins 9, 10 and 15 in IC2.

The counter is reset by closing switch S1, which may also be a push-button. This switch could be a limit switch placed as in Figure 7.4 to reset the counter each time the strip reaches one end of its travel. The output of the counter is a 4-bit binary number, counting from 0 to 15, so a maximum of 15 bars should be marked on the strip. With up to 9 bars it is possible to connect the counter output to a decoder such as a 4511 and 7-segment common-cathode LED display (see p. 108), which will show decimal values 0 to 9 as the encoder is moved (Fig. 7.9). It is also possible to use a 4033 decade counter/decoder in place of the 4520 shown in Figure 7.7.

Project 19 – Gray Code Position Sensor

This circuit is suitable for both linear and rotary sensors. As a rotary sensor it could be used with a wind vane to give remote reading of wind direction. As in Project 18 it is primarily intended for interfacing to a computer, so is powered by a 5V supply. The circuit consists of the diodes and NAND gate of

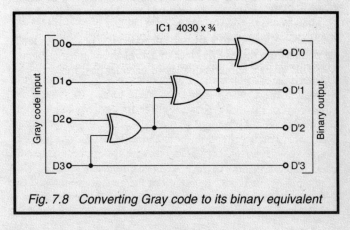

Fig. 7.8   Converting Gray code to its binary equivalent

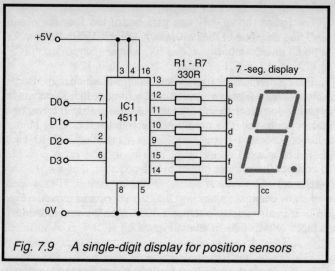

Fig. 7.9   A single-digit display for position sensors

Figure 7.7 repeated four times. IC1 has four gates so only one ic is needed. The diode pairs are mounted either side of the encoder strip one above the other so that they simultaneously read from the four areas in the columns of Figure 7.5. It may look as though the pattern of Figure 7.5 is haphazard but in fact it has some underlying regularities that make it very easy to decode. The decoding circuit in Figure 7.8 consists of three exclusive-OR gates. Their output is the binary value of the positions 0 to 15 shown in Figure 7.5.

If only positions 0 to 9 are to be decoded it is possible to feed the output from the ex-OR gates to a 4511 decoder as in Figure 7.9. This gives a numeric display of encoder position.

Chapter 8

NON-MECHANICAL SENSORS

There are dozens, if not hundreds, of non-mechanical sensors that have applications in control systems, especially in systems for process control. In this chapter we select a few of the most frequently used sensors, that are adaptable to a broad range of sensing functions. For a wider range of sensors, refer to BP273, *Practical Electronic Sensors*.

Light Sensors

A *light-dependent resistor*, or *LDR*, consists of a block of a semiconductor material such as cadmium sulphide or calcium selenide, with a pair of electrodes fused to the front surface (Fig.8.1). The electrodes are interdigitating so as to give a short but wide conducting path through the semiconductor. The semiconductor has high specific resistivity which varies according to the amount of light falling on it. The resistance of a typical LDR, the ORP12, is over $1M\Omega$ in darkness but falls dramatically to $2.4k\Omega$ at 50 lux (illumination by a 60W lamp at 1m), to 130Ω at 1000 lux (brightly-lit room) and much lower in bright sunlight. LDRs are sensitive to small changes in light intensity, are cheap, and are easy to use. They have a spectral response curve (sensitivity to light of different colours) similar to that of the human eye, which is sometimes an advantage. Their main disadvantage is that they are relatively slow to respond to changes in illumination. Response times are in the order of tens or hundreds of milliseconds. However, this is fast enough in many control applications. Figure 8.2(a) shows a typical connection for using an LDR. V_{OUT} increases as light intensity increases. The action of the circuit is reversed if R1 and R2 are exchanged.

For faster response, the most useful sensor is a *photodiode*. Figure 8.2(b) shows the typical connection for a photodiode. It is reverse-biased and a *leakage current* of a few nanoamps flows through D1 and on through R1. This generates a potential difference across R1. R1 has a high value to increase the pd produced, a typical value being $330k\Omega$. A consequence of this

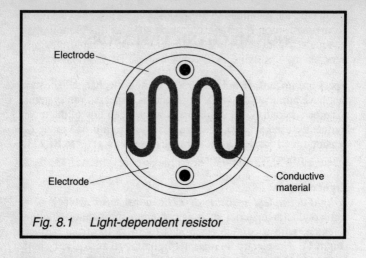

Fig. 8.1   Light-dependent resistor

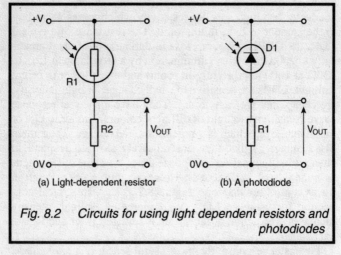

(a) Light-dependent resistor

(b) A photodiode

Fig. 8.2   Circuits for using light dependent resistors and
photodiodes

is that the circuit of Figure 8.2 is unable to deliver more than a
few picoamps to any subsequent stage. In other words, it has
high output impedance. It is necessary for the output to be fed
to an FET or to an op amp with FET inputs. The response time
of an ordinary photodiode is in the region of 250ns. This is

limited by the fact that the n-type and p-type layers of the diode form a capacitor. A response time as short as this is more than adequate for most control applications. More rapid response time, as little as 0.5ns, is possible with a PIV photodiode.

Heat Sensors

A *thermistor* consists of a sintered mixture of sulphides, selenides or oxides of nickel, manganese, cobalt, copper, iron or uranium. This mixture has the property that its resistance decreases as temperature increases. The relationship is not linear but is sufficiently close to linear over a limited temperature range. The equation is:

$$R_T = R_{ref}e^{-\beta(1/T - 1/T_{ref})}$$

R_T is the resistance in ohms at any given temperature T, which is expressed on the kelvin scale. The kelvin temperature is obtained by adding 273 to the Celsius temperature so, for example, $0°C = 273K$. R_{ref} is the resistance at a specified reference temperature T_{ref}. This is often taken as 25°C (= 298K). Values of R_{ref}, T_{ref}, and also β (a factor that depends upon the composition of the mixture) are obtainable from the manufacturer's data sheet or supplier's catalogue. The constant e is the exponential constant, with a value of 2.718 to 3 decimal places.

Thermistors are made in various physical forms such as rods, discs or beads. They may be bare or sealed in a glass or plastic capsule. They are suitable for measuring temperatures over the range –50°C to +300°C. One of the advantages of a thermistor (besides being cheap) is that it can be very small and can be inserted in a small space for measuring the temperature there. It is connected to the measuring circuit by a pair of wires which can be of reasonable length, allowing temperature to be measured remotely. One occasional disadvantage of a thermistor is that current has to be passed through it in order to measure its resistance. This generates heat in the thermistor and alters the resistance. This is only likely to be of significance at low temperatures or when the greatest precision is essential. In such cases a bridge circuit is used to minimise the current passing through the thermistor.

A thermistor is generally connected as part of a potential divider (Fig.8.3), with the thermistor either as shown or with

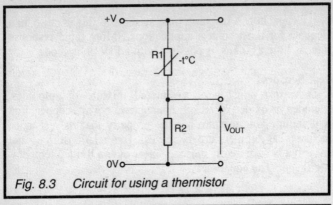

Fig. 8.3   Circuit for using a thermistor

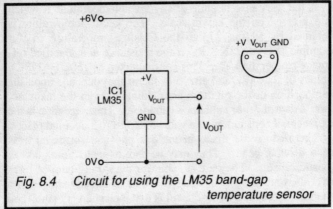

Fig. 8.4   Circuit for using the LM35 band-gap
temperature sensor

the resistors exchanged. In the diagram, the output voltage rises with increase in temperature. The voltage may be used to trip a transistor switch, possible through the intermediate stage of a Schmitt trigger. R2 is often a variable resistor to allow the output voltage to be adjusted. Another possible circuit is shown in Figure 6.6. If temperature is to be measured over a continuous range, the output can be fed to a circuit such as Figure 6.12. Changes of voltage are scaled and offset, possibly in preparation for analogue-to-digital conversion.

Note the marking '-t°' in Figure 8.3. This indicates that the thermistor has a *negative temperature coefficient*, which means

112

that its resistance decreases with increasing temperature, as we have already said. Such thermistors are referred to as *ntc thermistors*, in contrast to the type which have positive temperature coefficients and are used for different purposes.

A *band-gap temperature sensor* (Fig.8.4) provides an easily-interpreted output voltage. In the range 0°C to 110°C, the output voltage in Figure 8.4 varies from 0V to 1.1V. In other words, a temperature change of 1°C produces a voltage change of 10mV. This has an accuracy of ±0.4°C at 25°C and an accuracy of ±0.8°C over its whole range. For temperatures close to zero and below zero the sensor is wired as in Figure 8.5. This degree of accuracy applies to the LM35CZ. A slightly less accurate version, the LM35DZ (±0.8°C at 25°C), is available at lower cost. Both ics have rapid response time and low thermal capacity. Since they pass only a small current (56μA with a 5V supply) the heating effect is minimal. The LM35 can be operated on any supply voltage in the range 4V to 20V but, whatever the supply voltage, its maximum output is 1.1V at 110°C.

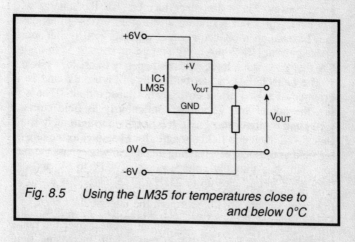

Fig. 8.5   *Using the LM35 for temperatures close to and below 0°C*

A bimetallic *temperature switch* is one of the simplest devices to install in a control system. The switch is designed to click open or closed at a preset temperature. Switches are made to operate at one of a number of temperatures in the range 40°C to 150°C, and with normally-open or normally-closed contacts.

Magnetic Sensors

The sensors described first under this heading depend upon the *Hall Effect*. When a current passes through a block of semiconductor material in a magnetic field, a potential difference develops across the block at right-angles to the direction of flow. This pd is detected and amplified by circuits on the same chip and used either to produce an output voltage proportional to the magnetic field strength, or to trigger a switching circuit. One of the advantages of these sensors is that they exert virtually no mechanical force on the mechanism being monitored. The UGN3132U device (Fig.8.6) is sensitive to field *direction;* it is triggered on (output low, close to 0V) by a magnetic south pole approaching the marked side of the sensor. It remains triggered until a reversed field is sensed, when its output rises to the supply voltage. The UGN3133U is sensitive to magnetic field *strength*, which must be positive (south pole toward sensor). It is switched off by a strong field, when a south pole is brought close to it, and switched off as the south pole is moved away. There are other members of this family with similar features but operating at different levels. In all cases they have an open-collector output which is able to sink appreciable current (10–20mA). With a pull-up resistor as in Figure 8.6, they can switch logic gates and operate transistor switches.

The UGN3503U has an outline as in Figure 8.6 and is an example of a Hall-effect device with linear output. That is to say, the output voltage varies continuously as field strength varies and is proportional to it. It is sensitive to extremely small changes in magnetic field strength, for example, to the changing field as the teeth of a rotating metal gear wheel pass the sensor. This has a supply voltage range of 4.5V to 6V and can respond at frequencies up to 23kHz. The 634SS2 is a similar device operating on 4V to 10V. It is enclosed in a 4-pin double-in-line ic package: pin 1 = 0V supply; pin 2 = output 2; pin 3 = output 1; pin 4 = +V. Its output is linear over the range −40mT to +40mT. Output 1 increases with increasing field strength, while output 2 decreases. The sensor can be used over the range ±100mT, but is non-linear outside ±40mT.

The switching devices have many applications as position sensors or proximity switches. Those with linear output are used for sensing rotation of mechanisms.

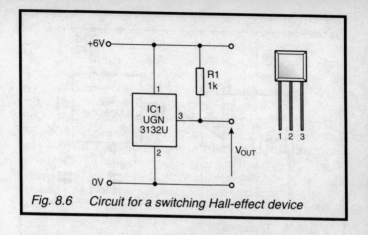

Fig. 8.6   Circuit for a switching Hall-effect device

Project 20 – Tachometer

A circuit for measuring frequency is often useful in control systems. In particular, it may be used for measuring the speed of rotation of motors and other machinery. The heart of the circuit in Figure 8.7 is the LM2917N frequency-to-voltage converter. A periodic signal is fed into pin 1 and a corresponding output voltage appears at pin 4. The input and output are related by the equation:

$$V_{OUT} = f_{IN} \times R3 \times C2 \times V_{cc}$$

V_{cc} is the reference voltage which is measurable at pin 6. This is 7.56V when the supply is 12V. A 470Ω resistor is used to drop the voltage to a level at which the internal reference circuit can hold V_{cc} constant. This ic can work on higher supply voltages up to 28V but the value of R2 must be increased to compensate for this.

The ic works with a wide range of input waveforms including square, triangular, pulse and sinusoidal waveforms. It is sensitive to 0.25V peak-to-peak signals. Usually a capacitor (C1) is included in the circuit to remove the DC level from the signal. In this project the input signal is generated by a photodiode (p. 109). This may be either a visible-light or infra-red

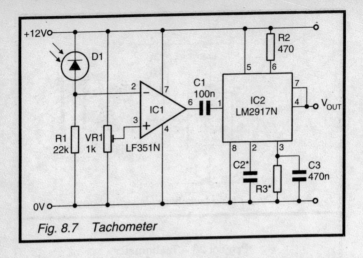

Fig. 8.7 Tachometer

diode. For measuring rate of rotation, one of the mechanisms shown in Figure 8.8 is used. The number of teeth or sectors required depends on the rate of rotation. In general, the faster the rotation the fewer teeth of sectors required, and the most suitable number is best found by experimentation. When the shaft is rotated a pulsed signal is generated. The amplitude of the pulse depends on the level of illumination, the sensitivity of D1 and the value of R1. It should be such that there is a difference of at least 0.1V between the high level (when the beam is unbroken) and the low level when the beam is broken. VR1 is adjusted so that the input to the (+) terminal of the ic lies midway between the two levels. The op amp acts as a comparator and, as the disc turns, its output alternates between a value close to 12V and a value close to 0V. This signal is ideal for the converter.

When deciding on the values of R3 and C2 we need to know the maximum rate of rotation of the disc and the maximum output voltage that is to correspond to this. If there is more than one tooth or sector on the rotating disc, the rate of rotation is multiplied by this to find the pulse frequency. If the output is to be fed to an analogue-to-digital converter for interfacing to a computer, a suitable maximum output is 2.5V or 2.55V. The maximum output can not be more than about 6.4V. For

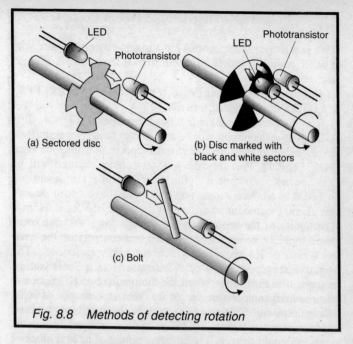

LED

Phototransistor

(a) Sectored disc

LED

Phototransistor

(b) Disc marked with
black and white sectors

(c) Bolt

Fig. 8.8   Methods of detecting rotation

example, suppose that the maximum rate of rotation or pulse frequency is 2000 per second and the maximum output is to be 2.55V. Then the equation gives:

$$RC = \frac{2.55}{7.56 \times 2000} = 1.6865 \times 10^{-4}$$

Select 10nF as a suitable value for C2, then R3 is given by:

$$R = (1.6865 \times 10^{-4})/(10 \times 10^{-9}) = 16865\Omega$$

For approximate readings a 16kΩ resistor is adequate, but this ic produces precision results with a linearity of about 0.3%, so it is feasible to use high-precision components (1% or better) for R3 and C2. In this case use a 16.9kΩ resistor or a 16kΩ resistor in series with a 1kΩ cermet preset.

The output may be fed directly to an A-to-D converter, or to a digital panel meter.

Project 21 – Time-Limited Heater Control

This is a thermostatic control for a mains-powered heater with a timer circuit to switch off the heater at the end of a selected period.

Before beginning this project, read the AC MAINS PRECAUTIONS on pages 38 to 40.

The temperature sensor is a band-gap sensor (Fig.8.4). It is unlikely that the circuit will be required to hold temperatures at levels close to 0°C, so the simpler connection may be used (IC1, Fig.8.9) Probably the highest setting required will be 50°C, when its output is 500mV. VR1 and R1 in series are intended to produce a matching range of voltages; with the values given, the maximum voltage at the wiper of VR1 is 545mV. The output of the sensor and the voltage from VR1 are compared by IC2a, an op amp connected as a comparator, the feedback resistor R4 providing a Schmitt trigger response. The negative supply to pin 4 of IC2 comes from a 7660 voltage inverter (see Fig.6.10). When the temperature of IC1 is below the required temperature as set by VR1, the output of IC2a swings positive. This positive swing is converted into an even sharper negative swing by IC2b, also connected as a comparator/Schmitt trigger. The negative output of IC2b is blocked by the diode D1 and is accepted as a logical low input by the first NAND gate. Here too we use the Schmitt effect to obtain a sharp on/off action for the circuit with minimal hesitation at the transition stage. The high output from this gate goes to the next gate, where is it NANDed with the output from the timer circuit (see below). The output of this gate is low when both its inputs are high; when the temperature of IC1 is below the set level AND the timer is set. Consequently, the outputs of the two final gates are both high. One turns on the transistor switch Q2, so energising the relay and turning on the heater. The other supplies current to an LED which indicates when the relay is activated.

S1 selects either the voltage from IC1 or the reference voltage from VR1. The voltmeter may be a moving-coil type or a digital panel meter and a suitable range is 500mV full scale. When switched to IC1 it gives a reading of room temperature (10mV/°C). When switched to VR1 it shows the temperature

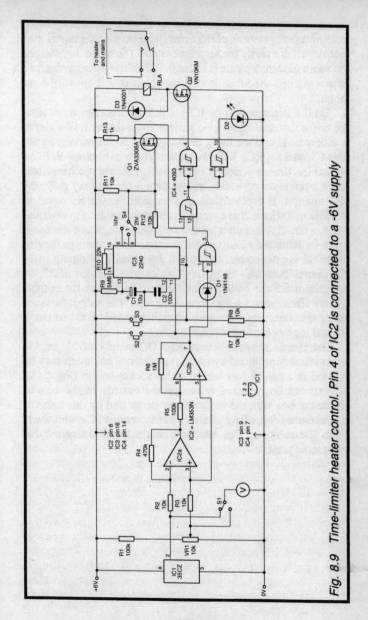

Fig. 8.9 Time-limiter heater control. Pin 4 of IC2 is connected to a -6V supply

119

to which the thermostat is set. Owing to voltage offset of the op amp and the hysteresis of the Schmitt input, the thermostat may not switch at exactly the set temperature. The heater is switched on when the temperature is about 0.5°C below the set point, and it is switched off when it rises to about 0.5°C above the set point.

Timing is performed by IC3, which incorporates an oscillator and counter to allow long periods to be timed. It is wired as a monostable and the basic timing period is determined by R9 and C1, and $t = RC$. With the values given in Figure 8.9, RC = 56, so the timing period is 56 seconds. Electrolytic capacitors have a tolerance of ±20%, so the actual period may differ by this amount. If precise timing is required, make R9 equal to 4.7MΩ and wire a 2MΩ preset in series with this. On resetting by pressing S3, outputs at pins 1 to 8 are all high and the oscillator is inhibited. The oscillator starts and counting begins when S2 is pressed and the output goes low. This circuit takes the output from one of pins 6-8 which give periods of 32, 64 and 128 times the basic period. With a 56s period, the outputs go low for 30 min, 1 h and 2h respectively. The output from the timer is inverted by the transistor switch based on Q1 so that a logical high is fed to the NAND gate.

The circuit requires a regulated DC supply of 5V or 6V, most suitably provided by a mains adapter. The circuit may be housed in a plastic box with a mains socket on top (Fig.2.13). IC1 should be mounted either on the outside of the box or inside the box with the walls nearby perforated by fine holes to allow circulation of air. In any event, mount IC1 well away from the relay, as this becomes warm when energised for protracted periods.

Chapter 9

CLOSED-LOOP SYSTEMS

Although this chapter is the one in which closed-loop systems are to be more fully discussed, there have been several instances of such systems in previous chapters. Figures 5.4, 5.10, 5.11 and 8.9 are examples. The principle of closed-loop control is illustrated in Figure 1.6, but this involves human response to generate the feedback. Figure 9.1 shows how the closed-loop principle operates in a purely automatic system, the circuit of Figure 8.9.

Closed-Loop Temperature Control

Apart from the temperature setting, the human input to the system centres on the timer, which is not actually part of the loop. The timer period is selected, the timer is set to begin operation of the heater and it is reset to end it, if it has not automatically ended already. Output from the timer goes to the control logic, the four NAND gates of IC4. It is the way that these gates are wired together which determines what the system actually does. The control logic exercises its control through the transistor switch Q2 and the relay. The heater warms the air of the room and this completes the forward action of the system. However, warmed air circulates in the room and eventually reaches the sensor, IC1. It is interesting to note that in the circuit diagram we draw IC1 on the left, as if it is IC1 which controls the heater. The block diagram of Figure 9.1 puts IC1 in its proper place, as the start of the feedback loop. After all, the heater would warm the room without there being any sensor present. The sensor is there simply to make the circuit operate automatically. The output from the sensor is compared with the set point, the voltage from the potential divider VR1. If the air is warmer than the set point, the heater is to be turned off; if the air is cooler than the set point, the heater is to be turned on. In other words, the feedback is negative. But the feedback voltage (or error signal) is too small to act as a logical level so it must be amplified. This is done partly by IC2a and completed by IC2b. These two amplifiers have Schmitt

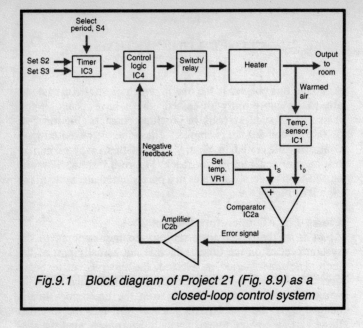

Fig.9.1 *Block diagram of Project 21 (Fig. 8.9) as a closed-loop control system*

inputs so they sharpen the response and provide hysteresis. The error signal is made more definite and not subject to minute fluctuations in temperature around the set point. Altering the characteristics of a signal in order to produce a beneficial effect is known as *signal conditioning*, and often plays an important part in a control system. In some systems, signal conditioning may take the form of filtering the signal. Indeed, in this system, the signal conditioning here is similar to that of a low-pass filter. In other systems a high-pass filter may be required to make the system function more effectively. Finally, the error signal is fed back to the control logic, so *closing the loop*. Once the initial settings have been made by the operator, the system functions automatically.

Proportional Control
In the circuit discussed above, the heater is either fully on or fully off. As discussed on p. 14, the room temperature oscillates two or three (possibly more) degrees above and below the set

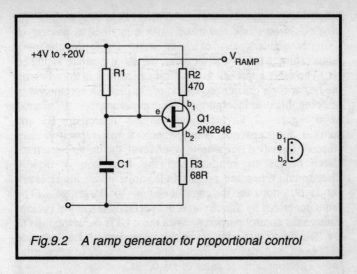

Fig.9.2   A ramp generator for proportional control

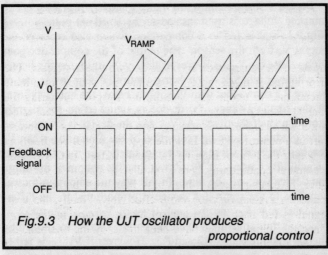

Fig.9.3   How the UJT oscillator produces proportional control

point. This applies even though the sensor is capable of responding to temperature changes as small as half a degree, as is the circuit of Figure 8.9. On p. 14 we mentioned a crude type of proportional control in which the operator switches on more heater bars when the room is excessively cold. A system of this kind could be made automatic, with a number of heaters or heater bars under control of a logic circuit. The further the room temperature is below the set point, the more bars are switched on. The other approach to proportional control is to switch on the heater for a greater proportion of the *time*. A common way of doing this is to incorporate a *ramp generator* into the circuit, as in Figure 9.2. Current flows through the resistor R1 and charges the capacitor. The pd across the capacitor rises steadily, but when it reaches a given level, the unijunction transistor begins to conduct and the capacitor is rapidly discharged. When the pd has fallen to a given lower level, conduction stops and the capacitor begins to charge again. The ramp generated by this circuit is not perfectly linear but is close enough for control purposes. With most UJTs the ramp falls to 2V. The time t taken for the ramp to rise depends on the value of R and C and may vary from a few milliseconds to a few minutes. The approximate value of t is 0.5RC.

Figure 9.3 shows how the ramp generator operates. The ramping voltage is used instead of the fixed set point voltage (Fig.9.1) and is fed to a comparator, which also receives the output V_0 from the sensor. The output of the comparator goes high whenever V_{RAMP} is greater than V_0, turning on the heater or whatever other device is being controlled. The lower part of Figure 9.3 shows that with V_0 slightly below the half-way level of the ramping range, the device is switched on for slightly more than half the time. As V_0 rises, the device is switched on for a gradually reducing proportion of the time until, when V_0 reaches the peak value of the ramp, the device is not switched on at all. By contrast, if V_0 is lower than the bottom of the ramp, the device is on all the time. In this way the amount of power supplied to the controlled device is proportional to the difference between V_0 and the peak level of V_{RAMP}. The peak of V_{RAMP} is thus equivalent to the set point. This is determined by the UJT and resistors R2 and R3. However if V_{RAMP} is fed to an op amp connected as an offset adjuster (see right-hand side of Figure 6.12) the range of the ramp can be adjusted. The set point is adjusted by VR2.

With proportional control, the power supplied to the controlled element (for example heater or motor) is proportional to the error signal. As the output of the element reaches the set point, the error signal is reduced, the power is reduced and the output approaches the set point more and more slowly. Theoretically it would approach the set point more and more slowly never actually reaching it but coming close enough for all practical purposes. However the *inertia* in a system, such as the turning inertia of a motor-driven mechanism or the thermal inertia in the coils of a heater, usually means that the response overshoots. Although proportional control gives a more stable response than straightforward error signal control, it still shows oscillations about the set point. In industrial control systems, we make use of additional control functions. One of these is *derivative control*, in which a term dependent on the *rate of change* of the error signal is added to the proportional signal. This may be done by op amps, but we will not go into the details here. The principle of derivative control is that, because the error signal is diminishing, its rate of change is negative. The error signal is reduced by an amount proportional to the derivative. The effect of this is that the total error signal reaches zero *before* the set point is reached. In terms of a heater, the heater is switched off a short while *before* the temperature has risen to the required level. With motor control the zero error signal cuts the power to the motor before the required speed is reached. In more sophisticated systems the total error signal becomes negative as the set point is approached and 'applies the brakes' to the system so that it homes smoothly on the set point.

Another form of control is known as *integral control*. Here a fraction of the proportional error signal is summed over time to produce a steadily increasing quantity, which is added to the proportional error signal. This is used to counteract any prolonged outside influence that is affecting the system. In the heater example, someone may have left the window open on a cold day. In a mechanical system there may be an unexpectedly large increase in the load. In either of these cases the response of the system needs to be offset from its normal response in order to cope with the special conditions. The integral term added to the proportional error term provides just the offset required.

Industrial control systems allow for proportional, derivative and integral control to be applied to lesser or greater degrees to tune the system to its working environment. We shall not go further into the electronic aspects of this complex topic, especially since computer control techniques allow similar control responses to be effected by software.

Designing for Regulation

A regulator system is one in which the output is to be brought to and held at a set point, which is infrequently altered, if ever. Fig 9.1 can be taken as a model of a regulator system. Although the temperature setting may be altered from day to day or from season to season, it is unlikely to be altered during a heating session lasting an hour. The stages in designing such a system are:

1 Controlled element: What type? What power rating?
2 Switching method: Chapters 2 to 5 provide the information, summarised in the Appendix.
3 Control logic: This may or may not be required, but may often be provided by a simple logic circuit consisting of a few NAND, NOR and INVERT gates. The circuits in various parts of this book provide a range of examples.
4 Control input: What control inputs are required? Just an ON/OFF switch? Or controls to select times, temperatures, speeds? How to link these to the logic circuits? Consult Chapters 2 to 5.

Step 1 to 4 provide the main control chain, which may be all that is required. Automatic systems usually require some kind of negative feedback loop to ensure that the system performs correctly under changing external conditions. Design of the feedback loop consists of the following stages:

5 Sensor: Chapters 7 and 8 suggest commonly-used sensors.
6 Generate the error signal: Chapter 6 has circuits for obtaining the error signal.
7 Close the loop: Feeding the error signal to the control logic. Chapter 6 has circuits for processing the error signal so as to facilitate the correct operation of the loop.

126

As a further example of regulation we make a case study of a circuit for controlling the speed of a DC motor. The motor is required to rotate a turntable at a steady speed in a shop-window display, turning it slowly for half a revolution, beginning each turn at 1-minute intervals. Consider the design stage-by-stage, as outlined above:

1 Controlled element: It is decided to use a low-power 12V DC motor, which was formerly used as a radiator fan motor in a car. The motor is to drive the turntable through a system of gears. The motor requires 2.5A when running, with an initial surge of 3A.

2 Switching method: The switch-mode speed control of Fig 5.6 is the basis of this. It operates equally well at 12V, except that the connection to pin 6 should be made to the on-chip regulator at pin 7 instead. The VN66AF maximum current is 1.46A, and since this particular motor requires a maximum of 3A the VN66AF is replaced with one of the many MOSFETs of higher rating, such as BUZ71, which is rated for 14A.

3 Control logic: This needs to be specially designed for each application, but is can usually be built up from a number of standard units. Figure 9.4 illustrates how some of these are used in this motor speed control project. Other logical units can be found in BP316 (see p. 197). The heart of the logic is a bistable which is set when the motor is to run and is reset when it is to stop. In Figure 9.4 we have a bistable made from two NAND gates. The two inputs are normally high; a low pulse from the timer sets the bistable, making its output go high; a low pulse from the pulse generator resets the bistable, making its output go low. The output from the bistable is used to interrupt the series of pulses from IC2 Figure 5.6 when the motor is to be stopped. A NAND gate is used; if the input from the bistable is low, no pulses pass through the gate and its output is constantly high. When the input from the bistable is high, pulses pass through the gate but they are inverted. A second NAND gate, connected as an inverter, is used to re-invert the pulses ready for sending to Q1. When the output from the bistable is low (reset), Q1 receives a constant low input and the motor does not

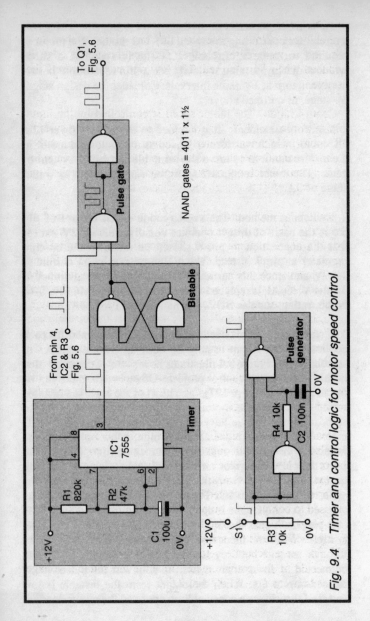

Fig. 9.4 Timer and control logic for motor speed control

NAND gates = 4011 x 1½

To Q1,
Fig. 5.6

Pulse gate

Bistable

From pin 4,
IC2 & R3
Fig. 5.6

Timer

8
4
3
7
R1
820k
6
2
R2
47k
1
C1
100u
IC1
7555
+12V
0V

Pulse
generator

R4 10k
C2
100n
0V

+12V
S1
R3 10k
0V

128

run. The pulse generator is another useful logic unit. There are several types of pulse generator, this one giving a short low pulse on a positive-going edge. The positive-going edge is produced when S1 is closed. The low output pulse resets the bistable.

4 Control input: The motor speed is controlled by the input voltage at pin 5 of IC2, Figure 5.6. For an open-loop system, this could be a potentiometer as shown in Figure 5.6, with a knob for manual operation. But this is intended to be an automatic system which operates continuously when switched on, so the next step is to design the feedback loop.

5 Sensors: A tachometer (Fig.8.7) is used, as described in Chapter 8. Choose values of C2 and R3 to give an output of about 2V at the required speed. The position of the turntable is sensed by a magnetic reed switch, represented by S1 in Figure 9.4. Two magnets are mounted diametrically opposite on the underside of the turntable so that they pass close to the reed switch as the turntable rotates. As a magnet passes the switch, it momentarily closes and a low pulse resets the bistable and stops the motor. The pulse is generated only as the magnet approaches the reed switch; after that the reset input to the bistable goes high again, so there is nothing to prevent the motor from starting again when the next pulse arrives from the timer. Bistables and pulse generators are invaluable units for assembling control logic.

6 Generate the error signal. In this example there are two error signals and two nested loops. The error signal from the position sensor is a low logic level when the turntable has not reached its next stopping position, and a high level when it has. The second error signal is produced by an op amp wired as a comparator, used to compare the output voltage from the tachometer, to a set-point voltage provided by a potentiometer (Fig.9.5). This arrangement allows the speed to be set to a wide range of values. For more accurate setting, fixed resistors are wired on either side of the potentiometer, to limit the settable voltage ranges between about 1.5V and 2.5V.

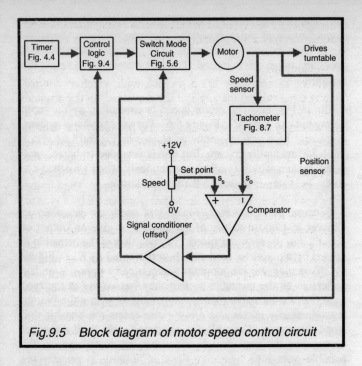

Fig.9.5   Block diagram of motor speed control circuit

7 Close the loops: The outer (position) loop needs no comparator or signal conditioning; simply connect the reed switch output to the control logic. In the inner loop, the 507C of the switch mode circuit accepts an input voltage between 0.25 and 0.75 of the supply voltage, in this case between 3V and 9V. The signal from the comparator requires an offset to put it approximately in the centre of this range. Use an op amp connected as the right-hand amplifier in Figure 6.12. Note that the control logic plays no part in speed control, so the loop is closed by connection to the switch mode circuit.

Another approach to closed-loop speed control is to take the signal from the photodiode of the tachometer and use a pulse rate comparator to compare its pulse rate with the pulsed output from a reference signal generator. The reference signal generator is set to produce pulses at a rate corresponding to the desired motor speed. The output from the pulse rate comparator is used to adjust the motor speed until the two pulse rates are equal.

Servo Control

A pilot of an aeroplane has a joystick with which to control (among other things) the angle of the elevators. In the original machines the joystick was connected to the elevators by a mechanical system of wires and levers, but today the control system is electronic. The same applies to a model aeroplane enthusiast flying a radio-controlled plane. The joystick is on the transmitting apparatus and radio signals relayed to the aeroplane are used to control the angle of its elevators. The motion of the control surfaces of the aeroplane is produced by a type of motor known as a servo-motor, usually shortened to servo. A flying model aeroplane usually has several servos aboard it, for moving the elevators, ailerons, and the rudder and also the throttle. They may be used for other functions such as retracting the undercarriage and dropping 'bombs'. Servos are also found in radio-controlled model cars, boats and land vehicles where they have basic steering and speed control functions as well as other more ingenious ones. Servos are not limited to radio-controlled models; when any kind of limited rotary motion or lever action is to be produced remotely, whether by radio-control or by hard-wired control, a servo is often used. They are particularly useful for producing the movement of arms (and legs, if any) of robots.

The principle of a servo is simple (Fig.9.6). A small low-voltage motor drives a set of reduction gears to rotate a lever. The lever is connected to the elevator or other mechanism that is to be moved. Usually the motion of the lever is limited to, say, 45° on either side of a central position. The servos used in model aeroplanes are small and light but, because of the gearing-down, they are able to exert a useful amount of force. Mounted on the same shaft as the lever is a rotary potentiometer. This acts as a potential divider producing an output voltage which depends on the position of the lever. This is used as a feedback signal.

One way of using the feedback signal is to set up a bridge in which the four arms of the bridge are made up of two potentiometers, the servo potentiometer and the control

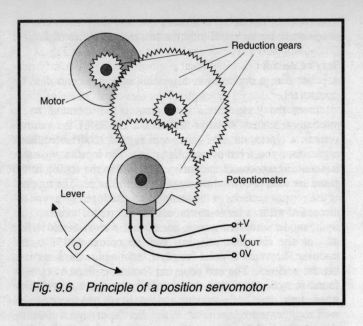

Fig. 9.6   *Principle of a position servomotor*

potentiometer. Any change in the setting of the control potentiometer causes the bridge to become unbalanced. This imbal-
ance is detected by the op amps which cause the motor to turn
in the appropriate direction to change the setting of the servo
potentiometer until the bridge is balanced again. One of the
problems with using ordinary potentiometers in this type of circuit is that they are never perfectly linear and are also subject
to wear, particularly as the wiper moves over the track every
time the servo changes position. Cermet potentiometers may be
used, as suggested in Project 22 but, for best results, use the
conductive plastic potentiometers specially made for use in
servo circuits. Unfortunately, the latter type are very expensive.

Servo systems control only the *direction* of the motor, to
make the lever home on a required position. Speed control can
also be incorporated, using a separate loop, usually nested
within the main servo loop as in the circuit of Figure 9.5. The
examples above make use of a potentiometer as a position
sensor, but other position sensors may be used. The circuit of
Figure 9.5, with its magnetic position sensor, is almost a servo

system, even through it is a crude one and does not allow the set point to be varied. Similarly, the microswitches of Project 15 provide servo-type control. A bar encoder as in Figure 7.5 may be used for sensing linear position and is particularly suitable for use in digital systems, including those controlled by computers.

Another way of controlling the servo is to use one of the ics specially intended for servo control. The ZN409CE is an example and a typical circuit is shown in Figure 9.7. The feedback signal from the servo potentiometer is fed to a pulse generator in the ic. The width of the pulses is related to the setting of the potentiometer. The control signal is a similar series of pulses usually produced by a manually operated pulse generator circuit. In most systems, the pulses vary in width between 1ms and 2ms, in which 1ms corresponds to the lever being turned 45° in one direction and 2ms corresponding to 45° in the opposite direction. A pulse length of 1.5ms puts the lever in a central position. The two pulse trains are compared by circuits in the ic and appropriate drive signal passed out to the drive transistors. This ic also has a dead band generator which produces pulses 1.5ms long. When the input signal matches these pulses sufficiently closely, the directional control is turned off, stopping the motor. The purpose of the dead band function is to prevent the motor 'hunting' (repeatedly changing direction) when the lever is sufficiently close to the required position. The width of the dead band is set by C5. The circuit is described more fully in Project 22.

The system of servo control described above is known as *pulse width modulation* (PWM). It is widely used in model control. A typical PWM radio controller generates a signal which consists of a series of pulses (often 4, but there may be more), each of which controls one of the servos in the model. This is known as a 4-channel system. The width of each pulse corresponds to the required position of each of the servos. The series of pulses is repeated about 50 times a second, so that any change in the position of the joystick is quickly transmitted to the model. At the receiving end the four pulses are separated out electronically and routed to the appropriate servo.

A more recent servo system uses *pulse code modulation* (PCM), in which the logic is appreciably more complicated.

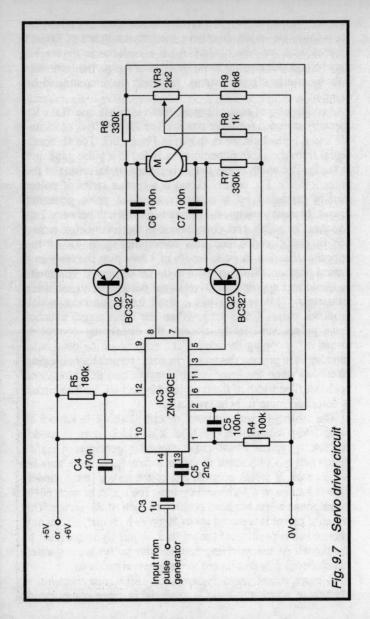

Fig. 9.7 Servo driver circuit

The transmitter sends a 7-bit code, which indicates numerically the required position of the servo. The eighth bit is a parity bit, to check that a valid code has been received. The receiver waits until a valid code is received, then passes the value on to the appropriate servo. If an extended period passes during which no valid codes are received, the receiver logic automatically resets the servos to suitable safe positions.

Project 22 – Servo Control Using a Driver IC

Figure 9.7 shows a typical application circuit for the ZN409CE servo driver ic. The servo potentiometer VR3 (preferably a cermet potentiometer) is coupled mechanically to the servo lever. The voltage at its wiper is proportional to the position of the lever within its range of movement. This voltage is sensed by pin 3 and used to generate a train of pulses of proportional width (1ms–2ms). This train is matched against a similar train coming from a pulse generator. Figure 9.8 shows a simple pulse

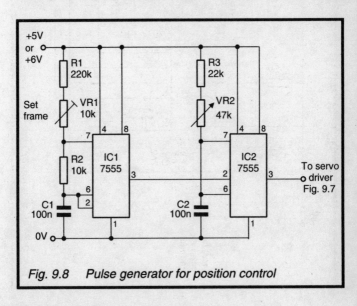

Fig. 9.8   Pulse generator for position control

generator. It consists of a 7555 ic wired as an astable, producing pulses every 18ms. This sets the length of the frame (the pulse repetition frequency that the ZN409CE is set to work at) and may be adjusted to the correct length by VR1. This is a preset potentiometer, used to set frame length once and for all. Each time the output from IC1 goes low, it triggers IC2, wired as a monostable to produce a pulse varying in width between 1ms and 2ms. Pulse width is controlled by VR2. The result of this is that the circuit produces a train of pulses 18ms apart and between 1ms and 2ms wide. Since pulse width is related to the position to which the lever is to move, the position of the lever is controlled by adjusting VR2. The control knob of VR2 may have a scale marked with the number of degrees through which the lever is to turn, ranging from $-45°$ (pulse length = 1ms) through the central position $0°$ (1.5ms) to $+45°$ (2ms). An oscilloscope is useful for setting up this circuit, though the circuit can be aligned by trial and error.

Chapter 10

CONTROL BY COMPUTER

This chapter describes how to use an IBM-PC or a similar computer as the heart of a control system. Figure 10.1 shows a typical system. Compared with the systems described in previous chapters, it is clear that most of the hardware (amplifiers, comparators, logic circuits) has been replaced by computer software. In spite of the substitution of software for hardware, the principles of control systems remain as before, so this chapter includes no new control theory. Instead we concentrate on the practical details of using the computer.

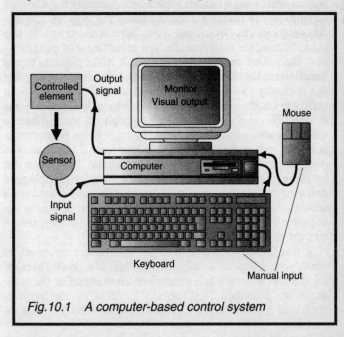

Fig.10.1   A computer-based control system

The computer programs are written in BASIC. They are all short and, even if the reader is unfamiliar with BASIC, there should be little difficulty in understanding them. Moreover, they are fully explained in the text and are selected to include a wide range of useful BASIC commands. Trying out these programs will give the reader a practical BASIC 'vocabulary'.

Interfaces

Before a computer can exercise any sort of control it must be put into contact with the outside world. Contact with the system operator is usually by way of the keyboard and the monitor screen. Contact with the controlled element and sensor(s) is by way of an *interface*, which is usually either a *port* or an interface *card*. A card is a circuit board which slots into a socket inside the computer. The reader may already have such cards as modem, a fax card or a sound card (such as SoundBlaster) residing in the sockets of his or her computer. A card is the best way of interfacing a control system to a computer but there are complexities in building them, including the required address-decoding circuits, which put them beyond the scope of this book. Instead, we shall describe how to make use of an existing port, the printer port. This means that it is not possible to use the printer at the same time as the control system is running, but this is usually no disadvantage. It makes it easier to switch from printer to control system and back again quickly if a *switch box* is used. This is a ready-made unit (though not too difficult to make at home) which is connected by cable to the printer socket on the rear of the computer. The box has a 2- or 3-position rotary switch and two or three 25-pin sockets. The printer can be plugged into one of these and the control system plugged into the other. If there is a third socket, this can be used for a second control system or perhaps for the probe of one of the analogue-to-digital converter units which allow the computer to be used as an oscilloscope.

If you find it inconvenient to put your printer out of action while your computer is being used as part of a control system, an alternative is to use a microcontroller instead of the computer, as described in Chapter 11. Most of the projects described in this chapter can also be controlled by a micro-controller.

In the IBM PCs the printer interface is generally referred to as LPT1. This port comprises three groups of input or output lines. Each group has an address, which specifies its location in the memory map of the computer. Most books state that the three groups, or *registers* of LPT1 are located at addresses 0378, 0379 and 037A, all addresses being expressed as hexadecimal numbers. In some models they may be at 0278, 0279 and 027A instead. However, in the author's IBM computer, the addresses are 03BC, 03BD and 03BE. Therefore, the first step is to find out the addresses in your own computer. Maybe they are given in the handbook but, more likely, you will need to run a configuration program. The IBM Configuration Utility is run by pressing the F1 key while the computer is counting the memory, almost immediately after it has been switched on. The information is displayed on four pages, or screens. Page 1 deals with general information about the system and memory. The address of the printer port is given under 'System Setup' on page 2. Here, under the entry 'Parallel Port' we find [Parallel_1 (3BC-IRQ7)]. The '3BC' or whatever other number may be listed there is the first address of the block of memory allocated to the parallel port, otherwise referred to as printer port LPT1. It is possible that other addresses may have been allocated to this port in other models of the PC or in versions from other manufacturers. In all the descriptions and programs which follow, we shall refer to these registers by just one address each, the one used in our model (6381) of the IBM-PC. The reader may substitute corresponding addresses if necessary.

Connection to the printer port is made with a microminiature D-type 25-pin plug. You may be able to buy this with the wire already soldered to the pins, or buy a standard printer lead and cut off the plug that goes into the socket on the printer. For simple applications, only a few of the pins need connections, in which case it is best to buy a bare plug and solder the wires where you need them. Figure 10.2 shows the layout of the plug at the printer port, the pins being viewed as seen when you stand behind the computer. The three registers are allocated pins as in the table on page 140.

Pins 18–25 are connected to the computer ground (0V) line. Any circuit connected directly to the computer must have its 0V line connected to one of these pins.

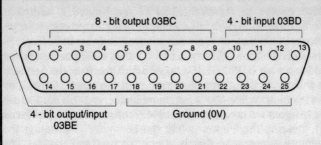

Fig.10.2   Printer port on an IBM PC, showing pins
allocated to each register

Address	Pin	Data bit	Function
03BC	2	0	8-bit output register; bit 0 is the
	3	1	least significant bit, bit 7 is the most
	4	2	significant bit. This register can also
	5	3	be read from as a check that the
	6	4	bits have been correctly set.
	7	5	
	8	6	
	9	7	
03BD	13	4	4-bit input; bits 0-3 not used. Bit 7
	12	5	is inverted (see Note 1 below).
	10	6	
	11	7	
03BE	1	0	4-bit input/output register; bits 4–7
	14	1	not used. Bit 2 is read and written
	16	2	to normally; bits 0, 1 and 3 are
	17	3	inverted (see Note 1 below).
	15	–	Not used.

So as to keep the information at one location in the book, we include the following notes here. However, they will be easier to understand after you have read the sections which follow, and have tried out some of the programs.

140

Note 1: 03BE is used as an output port in the same way as 03BC, except that three of its bits are inverted. A '1' written to bits 0, 1 and 3, produces a *low* output, and a '0' produces a *high* output. An extra step is needed when reading input to this register. Each bit must first be set to '1', then the input data either leaves it high or pulls it low, after which the data can be read. Setting the bits to '1' means writing a '0' to bits 0, 1 and 3, or a '1' to bit 2. When reading data, remember that bits 0, 1 and 3 are inverted so that a high input gives '0' and a low input gives '1'. The same applies to bit 7 of 03BD.

Note 2: There is a slight complication with two of the bits. The programs in this chapter are not affected by this, but it is mentioned as a possible cause of a program crash if one of these bits is accidentally set wrongly. Bit 7 of the 03BD register creates an interrupt (level 7) when it is made high. This causes the computer to stop what it is doing and jump to an interrupt service routine. But this action of bit 7 does not take place unless bit 7 has previously been enabled by setting bit 4 of the 03BE register to '1'. As we are using only bits 0 to 3 of that register, bit 4 will never become set and the interrupt bit 7 will never be enabled.

Outputting Data

Data is transferred through the port under the control of a *program*. The computer may be programmed either by machine code, assembler, or a high-level language. Machine code programs run the fastest, but writing programs in machine code is difficult, even though it is also fascinating. Assembler is a program which allows you to write a program by using a set of abbreviations for the various operations that the microprocessor performs. Then the assembler turns your instructions into machine code. Assembler is easier to write than machine code, but it is still hard enough. The easiest approach is to use a high-level language. The programs take longer to run and require more memory to store them, but control programs are never very long and high running speed is seldom required. High level languages include FORTRAN, PASCAL, C, and BASIC. Of these, we shall use BASIC which is a language most programmers are familiar with. There are various versions of

BASIC, of which we shall use GWBASIC. If you do not have a BASIC interpreter program on your hard disc, you will need to purchase one and install it before you can control the input and output registers. If you have some other version of BASIC, you will probably find that almost all the commands are identical with those of GWBASIC. The microcontroller described in Chapter 11 also runs on BASIC. Its range of commands is limited, but it has some useful additional commands specific to using that particular microcontroller. The way to use BASIC for transferring data is best explained by describing a few very simple projects.

Project 23 – Outputting a Single Bit

This project controls a single LED, flashing it on and off repeatedly. Once you have understood how to perform this elementary operation, you are well on you way to controlling almost anything. The LED is controlled through bit 0 of the 03BC register. All that is needed is a wire from that bit (pin 2 of the connector) and one from the ground (0V), which may be any one of pins 18–25. Figure 10.3 shows the circuit. The power supply is independent of the computer's power supply and *no direct connection must be made between the power supply line and any of the pins of LPT1, or any part of the computer or its peripherals.* The voltage is shown as +5V, which is best taken from a regulated 5V DC supply. A circuit for a 5V supply is given in the Appendix. When connecting up this and the other projects in this book to a computer *double-check all connections before switching on the power supply.* Failure to do this may result in damage to the ics of the computer port.

The command for sending (or *writing*) a data byte to an output port is:

OUT *address, value*

The *address* is that of the register, for example 03BC, and we prefix this by &H to indicate to the BASIC interpreter that this is a hexadecimal number. The value is the value of the byte considered as a binary number. For example, to output a '1' to

142

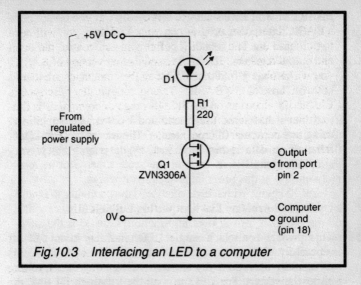

Fig.10.3   Interfacing an LED to a computer

bit 0, the value is 00000001 in binary. Each bit in the number
represents one of the 8 eight lines in register 03BC, with bit 0
on the right and bit 7 on the left. To use this value in the OUT
command we may express it as a decimal number (1) or as a
hexadecimal number (01). A decimal number has the disadvantage that it does not show clearly which bits are '1's and which
are '0's. For example, if the byte is 10001100 in binary, we can
see clearly that bits 2, 3, and 7 are '1'. Given the equivalent
decimal value, 140, the bit settings are by no means clear. As a
hexadecimal number, 8A, we soon learn that 8 is the same as
1000 binary, and A is the same as 1100 binary, so 8A is the same
as 10001100. As an example, to send a '1' to bit 0 of the 03BC
register (pin 2 on the port socket), the command is:

OUT &H03BC,&H01

The program also accepts single-digit hexadecimal numbers
such as &H1, but it makes the program easier to follow if we
use 2 bits, so as to identify all 8 lines of the register. Here is a
program to flash an LED connected to pin 2:

143

```
10  REM  ** Flasher 1 **
20  OUT &H03BC,&H01
30  FOR J = 1 TO 10000:NEXT
40  OUT &H03BC,&H00
50  FOR J = 1 TO 5000:NEXT
60  GOTO 20
```

Type this in *exactly* as it is printed and RUN it. Remember to distinguish between '0' (zero) and 'O' (letter 'oh'). The LED flashes on and off regularly until you stop the program by pressing CTRL and BREAK keys at the same time. Let us look more closely at this program to see how it works.

Line 10 begins with REM which tells the computer to ignore anything following on that line. We have used it to place a title on the program for our own information. Line 20 is the statement shown above, which sends a '1' to pin 2. The effect of this is to make the pin go to a high logical level. The value actually sent is 0000 0001, so really we are sending '0' to all the other pins at the same time. This turns on the transistor Q1 and so turns on the LED. To give ourselves time to see that the LED is on before we switch it off again, we have a FOR ... NEXT loop on line 30. This takes a variable which we have taken to be J (but it could be any other letter) and increases it by 1 at a time from 1 to 10000. In other words, it counts from 1 to 10000 before the program drops through to the next line. If you have a very fast computer you may find that even counting from 1 to 10000 does not give you long enough to distinguish the flashes, so you could increase the 10000 to 20000 or even more. On reaching line 40 the computer sends '0' to all the pins, pin 2 goes low and the LED is turned off. Line 50 is another 'delay' loop but takes less time as the count is only to 5000. The lamp flashes on for longer than it is off. Finally, line 60 sends the computer back to the beginning of the program to flash the LED again. The computer runs round and round the program and the lamp flashes until you break into the program and stop it. Now try a variation on the program:

```
10  REM  ** Flasher 2 **
20  CLS:OUT &H03BC,&H00
30  INPUT"Number of flashes";N
```

```
40  FOR K = 1 TO N
50  OUT &H03BC,&H01
60  FOR J = 1 TO 10000:NEXT
70  OUT &H03BC,&H00
80  FOR J = 1 TO 5000:NEXT
90  NEXT
```

When you run this program, the first thing that happens is
that the screen is cleared (CLS) and the LED is turned off if it
was previously on. Then the question "Number of flashes?"
appears on the screen. Key in any number greater than zero and
press RETURN (↵). The LED flashes the specified number of
times, then Ok appears on the screen to indicate that the program is finished. The flashing part of this program (lines 40 to
70) is the same as lines 20 to 50 in the previous program but
now these lines have been included in a FOR...NEXT loop.
This begins on line 30, and uses a different loop variable, K,
which is made to increase from 1 to N, where N is the number
of flashes requested. The computer runs around the outer loop
N times, flashing the LED once each time round. Note the way
in which we can use the keyboard to tell the computer how
many flashes are requested. The INPUT command, followed by
a message and a variable name, makes the computer wait until
you have keyed in a number (which value is given to N) and
pressed RETURN. Another point to note is that here we have
two FOR J ... NEXT loops, each of which is completed by the
NEXT (actually NEXT J, but we do not need to specify the J)
on the same line. These two are surrounded by the FOR
K...NEXT loop, which begins on line 30 and ends with NEXT
(really NEXT K) on line 80.

The final program needs two LEDs, each with its own transistor to switch it. In other words, build Figure 10.3 a second
time and connect it to pin 3 (bit 1). Here is the program:

```
10  REM  ** Flasher 3 **
20  FOR K = 1 TO 5
30  OUT &H03BC,&H01
40  GOSUB 130
50  OUT &H03BC,&H03
60  GOSUB 130
```

```
70   OUT &H03BC,&H02
80   GOSUB 130
90   OUT &H03BC,&H00
100 GOSUB 130
110 NEXT
120 END
130 FOR J = 1 TO 20000:NEXT
140 RETURN
```

The main program is enclosed in a FOR K...NEXT loop from lines 20 to 120. This time we specify that the loop will be run 5 times. Within the loop we send the values 01, 03, 02, 00 to the port in succession. The results are:

01	in binary, 00000001	LED 1 is lit
03	in binary, 00000011	LEDs 1 and 2 are lit
02	in binary, 00000010	LED 2 lit
00	in binary, 00000000	Neither LED is lit

An interesting feature of this program is the GOSUB command. Instead of repeating 'FOR J = 0 to 20000:NEXT' after each byte is sent to the port, we type it just once on line 130 as a subroutine. Each time the program comes to a GOSUB 130 command, it jumps to line 130 and runs the delay loop. After this it goes to line 140 where it is told to RETURN. It returns to the place it jumped from. With a subroutine at the end of the program we need an END statement to mark the end of the main program. Otherwise after the computer has reached line 120 for the fifth time, it will run straight into the subroutine without having been told by a GOSUB to go there, and this will cause an error message to be displayed.

These three programs illustrate how you can control LEDs from a simple BASIC program. For practice, work with one LED and make it flash according to several different sequences. Also use two LEDs and make them flash alternately like the lamps at a railway crossing (a good project for the railway modeller). Finally, set up three LEDs, red, yellow and green, and program them to operate the traffic light sequence. Building and controlling model traffic lights could make an attractive project. Read pages 156–160 if you have problems in working out which values to use in OUT commands.

Isolation Techniques

Most of the circuits described in this chapter can be connected directly to the port, especially those that control or receive input from a simple circuit with low voltage levels. However, the more complicated the circuit the greater the possibility of wiring it incorrectly. Also a circuit with inductive components (motors, relays, solenoids) may be subjected to high voltage spikes at times. There are two ways of isolating the external circuit from the computer circuit:

1 Buffer ic: These contain logic gates, usually 4, 6 or 8, which act as a link between the computer and the external circuit. Buffers may be *non-inverting*, in which the output takes the same logical state as the input, or *inverting*, in which a high input produces a low output and the other way about. A popular CMOS non-inverting buffer is the 4050 (Fig.10.4a) which has 6 individual buffers in one package. This is also available in 74HC series as 74HC4050. Figure 10.4b shows how the buffer may be wired between the computer and the circuit of Figure 10.3. However, when its output is low, a CMOS buffer gate sinks enough current (about 6mA) to light an LED

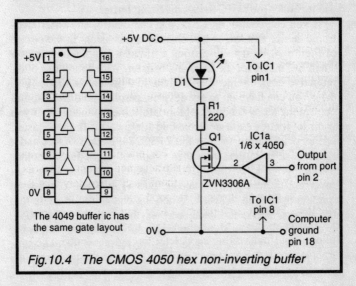

The 4049 buffer ic has the same gate layout

Fig.10.4   The CMOS 4050 hex non-inverting buffer

147

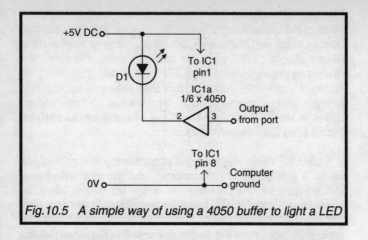

Fig.10.5 A simple way of using a 4050 buffer to light a LED

reasonably brightly. Figure 10.5 shows how to connect it. A low input gives a low output which draws current through the LED, switching it on. With this connection the programs work the other way round to that described above. To obtain the same action, either change the output statements in the program or use the 4049 (or 74HC4049) inverting buffer.

If you can control an LED, you can control any other electronic device that can be switched by a transistor. In the circuit of Figure 10.4b, try substituting a filament lamp, a buzzer or a small DC motor for the LED and resistor. With a motor or other inductive device remember to include a protective diode (Fig. 3.1). You can have up to six devices, perhaps all different, and control the lot by sending appropriate values to the port. If you want to control eight devices, one for each bit in the register, use an octal buffer, such as the 74HC244. Details of this and a range of other buffers appear in suppliers' catalogues. Another useful buffer ic is the 74HC125, which contains four non-inverting buffers with 3-state outputs (Fig.10.6). The 3-state outputs operate in this way. When the enable pin is made low the buffers act in the same way as those of the 74HC4050, except that they can supply or sink a larger current. When the enable input of a gate is made high, the output of the gate takes on a high-impedance state. This means that it is, in effect, disconnected from the line to which it is wired. This facility allows

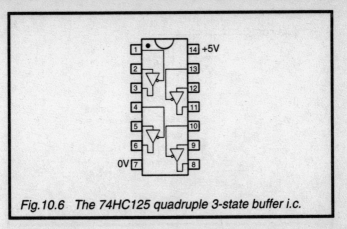

Fig.10.6   The 74HC125 quadruple 3-state buffer i.c.

several buffers to have their outputs wired to the same line but only the enabled one is able to send signals along that line (see Fig.10.11 later). The enable inputs can be controlled either by the external circuitry itself or by output from the computer. If you do not wish to make use of the 3-state facility, simply connect the enable input permanently to the +5V line.

2 Opto-couplers. These have been described on pages 28 and 32 and obviously have applications in totally isolating the external circuit from that of the computer. A typical connection is shown in Figure 10.7. Since optocouplers are available with a thyristor or a triac instead of the transistor, they are suitable for controlling a large variety of devices. In all cases the transistor, thyristor or diac circuit is completely isolated from that of the computer.

Techniques for isolating inputs are described on page 156.

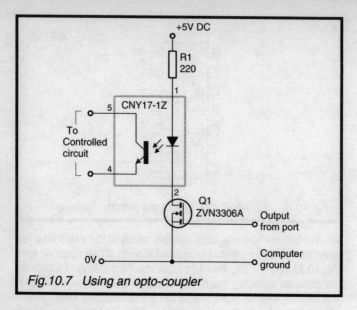

Fig.10.7 Using an opto-coupler

Inputting Data

In this section we look at input interfaces and BASIC programs for using them.

Project 24 – Monitoring a Push-Button

This project illustrates the elementary operation of reading a 1-bit input. The input is provided by the circuit of Fig 10.8. The input sent to the computer indicates the state of the push-button. The input is high when the button is not pressed, and low when it is pressed. The BASIC command for reading the input is:

$$A = INP(address)$$

A is a variable, which is assigned the value present at the addressed register. We can use any other variable name instead of A. Note that brackets are essential in this command, but are not to be included in the OUT command. The address is the register address in hexadecimal, which may be &H03BC, &H03BD or &H03BE, depending on which register we are

150

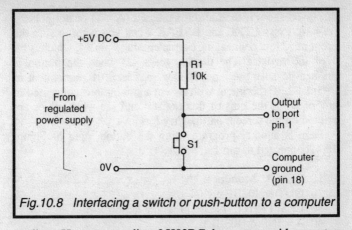

Fig.10.8 Interfacing a switch or push-button to a computer

reading. However, reading &H03BC does not provide an actual input; it only reads what has already been written there by the computer. In this project we will use the register at 03BE, and here is a program to do this:

```
10  REM ** Monitor 1 **
20  OUT &H03BE,&H04
30  A = INP(&H03BE)
40  PRINT A
50  FOR J=1 TO 10000:NEXT
60  GOTO 20
```

Line 20 sets the output levels of the bits to all *high*. Note 1 on p. 141 explains why this is necessary. For the inverted bits (0, 1, and 3), we send a *zero* to the register. Because bit 2 is not inverted, we send a '1' in the normal way. Thus, for the 4 bits, we send '0100', equivalent to 4 in decimal and hexadecimal. This sets the outputs from the register to all high, but they are immediately pulled down if they are receiving a low input. Line 30 reads the register and assigns the value read to A. If the key is not pressed, the input is high but this is read as '0', which is printed on the screen at Line 40. If the button is pressed, the low input from the button circuit pulls the input low, but the value displayed on the screen is '1'. After the delay (line 50) the program repeats and another value is printed. The values

151

displayed show if the button is pressed (A = 1) or not pressed (A = 0). Press CTRL and BREAK when you want to stop the program. Now connect the button circuit to pin 14, which is bit 1 of the register. The display reads '2' when the button is pressed because the input is now read as 0010, equivalent to decimal 2. Experiment with two or more buttons connected to any or all of the pins of this register and see what values are printed on the screen, particularly for pin 16.

Here is another program using the button input of Figure 10.4, connected to pin 1:

```
10  REM ** Monitor 2 **
20  OUT &H03BE,&H04
30  CLS: PRINT "Please press the button"
40  A = INP(&H03BE)
50  IF A=0 THEN 40
60  CLS: PRINT "Button pressed - Thankyou!"
```

The computer reads the input at line 40. Line 50 sends the computer back to line 40 if A equals zero (button not pressed). The computer is sent back every time until A is *not* zero. When the button is pressed, A equals 1 so the computer drops through to line 60, where is prints a new message. The CLS command clears the screen before printing messages. This program works for bits 0, 1 and 3 because it takes into account the inverted operation of the registers. For bit 2 we need to hold the button down before running the program, and it ends when the button is released. The messages are wrong in this case, but the program could be revised so as to be used for detecting a broken contact instead of a made one. A way of making all inputs read in the correct (non-inverted) way is given later.

It is possible with buttons connected to two or more pins to modify the program to detect *which* button is pressed and to display different messages accordingly.

Project 25 – Using Input and Output

The program listed above is able to detect an input from any circuit that has a 1-bit logic level output. Figure 10.9 shows

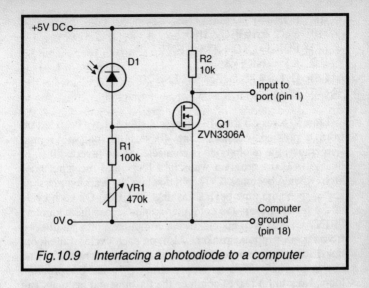

Fig.10.9 Interfacing a photodiode to a computer

how a photodiode is used as a sensor which produces a low output when light is striking the photodiode and a high output when the light is cut off. It could be used to detect when an intruder breaks a light beam. A beam of visible or infra-red light is directed on to the sensor from the other side of the room, corridor or doorway. This circuit also works with daylight as the light source. VR1 sets the light level at which the output changes. We connect the photodiode circuit to pin 1. An LED is connected to pin 2 as in Figure 10.3. Here is one of many possible programs to use this sensor:

```
10  REM ** Security **
20  CLS
30  OUT &H3BC,&H00
40  OUT &H3BE,&H04
50  A = INP(&H03BE)
60  IF A = 1 THEN 40
70  PRINT"INTRUDER DETECTED"
80  OUT &H03BC,&H01
90  PRINT CHR$(7)
```

```
100   FOR J=1 TO 10000:NEXT
110   OUT &H03BC,&H00
120   FOR J=1 TO 10000:NEXT
130   K$ = INKEY$
140   IF K$ = "" THEN 80 ELSE 20
150   END
```

Line 30 turns off the LED in case it should have been left on from a previous session. Line 40 sets the output to high (remember, the photodiode is connected to an inverted bit). In lines 50–60 the program waits in a loop until the input goes high, when A becomes 0. Then it displays the warning message and at the same time begins flashing the LED. On each cycle of the flashing loop, the computer comes across the command PRINT CHR$(7). This makes the computer emit a short beep from its built-in loudspeaker. Also, on each cycle of the loop, line 130 tests the keyboard to see if any key is pressed. If no key is pressed, K$ is an empty string ("") and the program loops back to line 80 to continue the flashing and beeping. But if any key is pressed, K$ is not empty and the 'ELSE' part of line 140 comes into action, sending the computer back to the beginning of the program. In other words, pressing any key resets the system.

In an actual intruder system there might be several other sensors, such as reed switches on doors and windows, passive infra-red sensors, and pressure mats. Each of these would be interfaced to a different bit in register 03BE. There could also be several output devices such as a solid-state siren, and a relay to flash a mains-powered lamp, or perhaps to turn on security lighting around the building.

The following program has an entirely *different function*, yet uses the same hardware as in Figures 10.3 and 10.5. It is a good illustration of the advantages of using a computer as the heart of a control system. The action of the system can be modified or even completely changed simply by using different software. A wholly hardware system would need radical reconstruction to convert it from the security system described above to the counting system described below. Here we just alter the software to:

154

```
10    REM ** COUNTER **
20    CLS:N=0:OUT &H03BE,&H04
30    PRINT"Counting . . ."
40    OUT &H03BC,&H00
50    GOSUB 150
60    IF A=1 THEN 50
70    N=N+1
80    PRINT N
90    GOSUB 150
100   IF A=0 THEN 90
110   IF N<10 THEN 50
120   PRINT"Maximum is 10"
130   OUT&H03BE,&H01
140   END
150   OUT &H03BE,&H04
160   A=INP(&H03BE)
170   RETURN
```

The counter operates by counting the number of times the light beam is interrupted. It might be counting objects passing on a conveyor belt, people entering a room, or cars entering a car-park. It displays a message and turns on the LED when the maximum number of interruptions (10 in this example) is reached. The number of objects counted is N and this is set to zero at the start of the program. Line 40 extinguishes the LED if it is already on. Then the program branches to a subroutine to find out if the beam is interrupted or not. If $A = 1$, it is not interrupted and the program loops back to line 50 to be sent back to the subroutine. The program waits in this loop until $A = 0$, showing that the beam is interrupted. Then it increments N and displays the new value. The program operates so quickly that it could go back to the beginning many times while the beam is interrupted by a single person or object, and so build up a unduly high count. To prevent this, the program is sent to the subroutine again in line 90. On its return, A is tested to see if the beam in not interrupted, in other words to see if the object or person has moved on, out of the beam.

The program waits in this loop until the beam is no longer interrupted. At line 110, N is tested to see if it has reached 10.

If not, the program repeats from line 50, if N = 10 the message is displayed and the program ends.

Input Buffers
The buffers described on pages 147–149 may also be used for conveying data in the opposite direction, from the external circuit to the input port of the computer (Fig.10.10). The 74HC125 is useful if input lines are limited in number; several buffers may be wired to the same line (Fig.10.11). The computer can select which one to read from by making its enable line low.

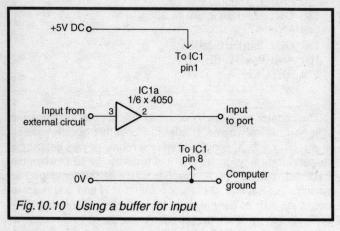

Fig.10.10 Using a buffer for input

Phototransistor optocouplers may also be used for input, as in Figure 10.12.

Bits and Values
In all except one of the programs above, we have interfaced the LED, the sensor and the push button to bit 0 of the registers. This means that the value of a low input to pin 0 is 0 and that of a high input is 1. If the input or output is an inverted one, the values are the other way round, but we shall ignore this complication until later. If the computer is asked to print the input A, it prints either '0' or '1'. The other bits in the register, all have zero value when they are low, but these values when they are high:

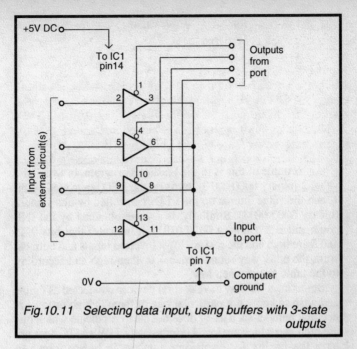

Fig.10.11 Selecting data input, using buffers with 3-state outputs

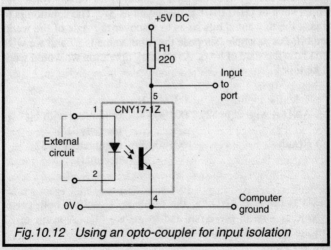

Fig.10.12 Using an opto-coupler for input isolation

Bit	High Value
0	1
1	2
2	4
3	8
4	16
5	32
6	64
7	128

An example of this is in the Flasher 3 program, in which the value 2 (binary 0000 0010) turns on the LED controlled by bit 1, and the value 3 turns on the LEDs controlled by bits 1 and 2 (binary 0000 0011). Similarly, if a value obtained by the INP command is 37(binary 0010 0101), it indicates that bits 0, 2, and 5 are high and the rest are low. Inverted inputs and outputs, work the other way round: value = 0 when high and according to the table above when low.

Sometimes we may have several devices connected as inputs and wish to know if a particular one of them is high or low. A decimal number such as 37 does not clearly indicate which bits are high and which are low. Unfortunately, GWBASIC does not have the facility for displaying numbers in binary form. An input such as 0010 0101 is displayed as 37. The solution is to mask the unwanted bits so as to discover the state of the wanted bit. For example, suppose the input value is 37 and we wish to know the state of bit 6. As a binary operation we would work like this:

Take the input:	00100101	
AND it with 2^6 (=32)	00100000	(a number with bit 6 the only '1')
Result	00100000	(equivalent to 32 decimal)

This is bit-wise ANDing; the result is '1' only if both corresponding bits in the input and in 26 are '1'. A result of 32 means that bit 6 is high. Looking at bit 5:

```
Take the input:          00100101
AND it with 2^5 (=16)    00010000    (a number with bit 5 as
                         --------     the only '1')
Result                   00000000
```

A result of zero means that bit 5 is low. This operation can be translated into a BASIC command:

$$X = INT((A \text{ AND } 2^N)/2^N)$$

A is the input, N is the number of the bit to be evaluated and (since we have extended the calculation above by dividing the result by 2^N) X is either 0 or 1, depending on the state of bit N.

The main difficulty with using the printer port for input is that some bits of 3BD and 3BE are inverted and some are not. This makes little difference for single-bit outputs and inputs. We can combine masking out the bit as above with inverting the bit:

$$X = INT((NOT \text{ } A \text{ AND } 2^N)/2^N)$$

Multibit inputs are only slightly more difficult to manage. The programming solution is to use the exclusive-OR operator. When a bit is ex-ORed with a 0, its state is unchanged. When ex-ORed with a 1, its state is inverted. To invert some bits of a multi-bit input but not others, we exOR the input with a number which has 1's for the bits that are to be inverted, and 0's for those that are not. The details depend on which register is being used:

1 Using 03BE as a 4-bit input/output: Ex-OR the input with 1011 (decimal 11 - eleven), a number with bits 0, 1 and 3 high. If A is the value read from the input or to be written as an output, and B is the actual value, then the BASIC command for converting A to B is:

$$B = A \text{ XOR } 11$$

```
For example:   A    is      0101    (decimal 5)
               XOR  with    1011    (decimal 11)
               B    is      1110    (decimal 14)
```

159

In B, bits 0, 1 and 3 are inverted.

2 Using 03BD as a 4-bit input: Use of this register is further complicated by the fact that we are using bits 4 to 7 and ignoring bits 0 to 3. The first step is to mask out the lower four bits by ANDing the input value C with 11110000 (240 decimal):

For example:

C is	10101000	(decimal 168)
AND with	<u>11110000</u>	(decimal 240)
D is	10100000	(decimal 160)

This gives the four top bits as in C and turns the unwanted bottom 4 bits into zeros. Divide by 16 to remove these, then ex-OR with 8 to invert the top bit (formerly bit 7)

D becomes	1010	(decimal 10)
XOR with	<u>1000</u>	(decimal 8)
E is	0010	(decimal 2)

These operations are combined in one BASIC command:

$$E = (C \text{ AND } 240)/16 \text{ XOR } 8$$

3 Using 03BD with 03BE as an 8-bit input: An 8-bit input can be obtained by using both registers simultaneously. Input from 03BE (call it A) provides bits 0 to 3; input from O3BD (call it C) provides bits 4 to 7 after masking as above. No division by 16 is needed, as bits 4 to 7 retain their positions. Then we add the inputs from the two registers and ex-OR their sum with 139 to invert the bits where necessary. The statement is:

$$F = A + (C \text{ AND } 240) \text{ XOR } 139$$

This command is suitable for reading the 8-bit value from an ADC. An example is the temperature reading obtainable from the band-gap sensor circuit described in Project 17, p. 97.

Motor Control

A low-voltage DC motor such as is used in robots and models is switched on or off by the circuit of Figure 10.13a. Note that

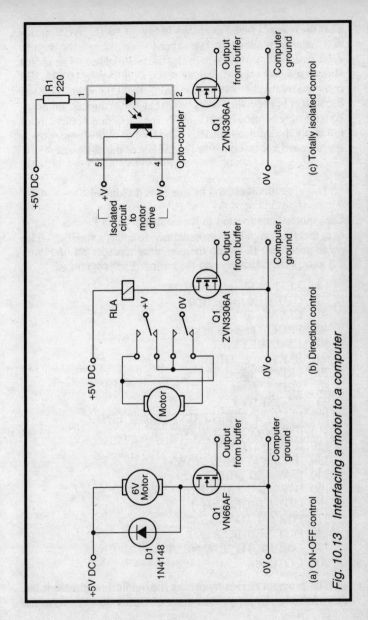

Fig. 10.13 Interfacing a motor to a computer

161

a buffer is used, wired as shown in Figure 10.4b. A 6V motor will reach a moderately high speed even though the supply voltage is only 5V. Alternatively, use a 3V motor. The motor is reversed using a double-pole relay, as in Figure 10.13b. To completely isolate the motor from the computer, perhaps because it is necessary to operate it at 6V or higher, an opto-coupler may be used (Fig.10.13c). The LED side of this circuit is exactly the same as Fig.10.3. The 0V rail of the motor power supply need not be connected to the 0V of the computer.

Project 26 – Motor Speed Control

The motor is connected to the computer as in Figures 10.13a or c, and the computer is programmed to act as a variable-width pulse-generator. In effect, the computer replaces all of Figure 5.5 except the transistor and the motor. The program is:

```
10   REM ** Motor control **
20   OUT &H03BC,&H00
30   CLS:W=10
40   PRINT "Press G to start"
50   K$=INKEY$
60   IF K$<>"g" THEN 50
70   PRINT "Speed = 10"
80   PRINT "Press + or -"
90   K$=INKEY$
100  IF K$="s" THEN PRINT "STOP":END
110  IF K$="-" THEN W=W-1
120  IF W<0 THEN W=0
130  IF K$="+" THEN W=W+1
140  IF W=>20 THEN W=20
150  IF K$<>"" THEN PRINT "Speed = ";W
160  OUT &H03BC,&H01
170  FOR J=1 TO W:NEXT
180  OUT &H03BC,&H00
190  FOR J=1 TO 20-W:NEXT
200  GOTO 90
```

The program begins by setting the output low in case it has been left high by a previous session. Speed depends upon the

162

pulse width, which can be 0 to 20, and this is set to half-speed, W=10, in line 30. In lines 40 to 60 the computer waits for the user to press "G" before starting the motor. Line 70 displays the initial speed and line 80 asks the user to press "+" or "–" keys to vary the speed. Line 90 looks for input from the keyboard but, if no key is pressed, the program continues. Lines 100 to 150 result in no further action. When it comes to line 160 it begins a high output pulse and the motor starts. The pulse lasts until J has been counted from 1 to W. Then the output is made zero and a second loop times the low period between pulses to be 20-W. The computer then loops back to line 90 to produce the next pulse. With W=10 a series of half-width pulses is sent to the motor. The total count of lines 170 and 190 is 20, independently of the value of W. This takes about 0.5ms on the author's computer so the pulse frequency is about 2kHz. The pulse train continues unchanged for as long as no key is pressed. But the keyboard is interrogated each time around the loop, at line 90 and, if a significant key is pressed, the computer takes appropriate action. Line 100 stops the motor if key S is pressed. Line 110 reduces W if the minus key is pressed. Line 120 prevents W becoming less than 0. Line 130 increases W if the plus key is pressed and line 130 prevents W becoming more than 20. Line 150 detects if any key has been pressed and displays the new speed.

The program is easily tailored to meet special requirements. The starting value of W could be made 0 or some other value. The minimum value of W could be made, say 5, so that the motor never runs very slowly. The number of speed steps could be made greater or less.

It is possible on the PC to run GWBASIC at the same time as Windows programs. With most programs this makes no apparent difference to the operation of the GWBASIC program. However fast-acting programs such as this one are periodically delayed for an instant while the computer switches its attention to other programs running at the same time. This causes the motor speed to become jerky. When using this program ensure that no other programs are running.

A computer can be programmed to control a stepping motor, so replacing the SAA1027 of Figure 5.7. The typical 4-phase motor is driven through four transistors (Fig.10.14), acting to

163

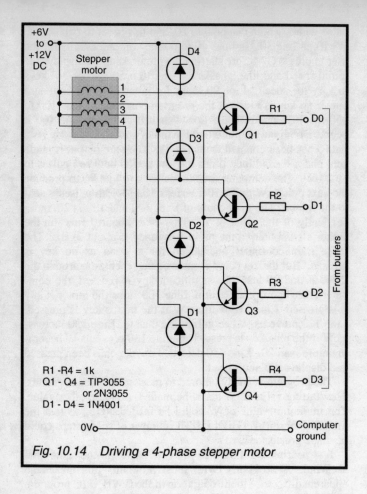

Fig. 10.14   Driving a 4-phase stepper motor

switch on the coils according to a sequence, in which 1 represents the coil being energised and 0 represents it not being energised:

Step	Coil 1	Coil 2	Coil 3	Coil 4
0	1	0	1	0
1	0	1	1	0
2	0	1	0	1
3	1	0	0	1

The sequence repeats indefinitely for as long as the motor is required to turn. Running the sequence in the reverse order makes the motor turn in the opposite direction. The codes to be sent to the register are 10, 6, 5 and 9 (in decimal). There is no simple mathematical way in which these can be derived, so the best approach is to store the values in an array, as in this program:

```
10   REM ** Stepper motor control**
20   OUT &H03BC,&H00
30   CLS:P=10:F(0)=10:F(1)=6:F(2)=5:F(3)=9
40   D=1:N=0:M=0
50   PRINT "Press G to start"
60   K$=INKEY$
70   IF K$<>"g" THEN 60
80   PRINT "Speed = 10"
90   PRINT "Press + or -, Press F or R"
100  K$=INKEY$
110  IF K$="f" THEN D=1
120  IF K$="r" THEN D=-1
130  IF K$="s" THEN PRINT "STOP":END
140  IF K$="-" THEN P=P+1
150  IF P<0 THEN P=0
160  IF K$="+" THEN P=P-1
170  IF P>20 THEN P=20
180  IF K$<>"" THEN PRINT "Speed = ";P
190  M = N MOD 4:IF M<0 THEN M=4+M
200  OUT &H03BC, F(M)
210  N=N+D
220  FOR J = 1 TO (20-P)*1000:NEXT
230  GOTO 100
```

This program has similar structure to the previous program. Now the pulse width variable W is replaced by P, controlling

165

the time for a complete cycle through the 4 steps (= 30° turn on a 7.5° motor). The array F() contains the four output codes. D is the direction, 1 for forward, -1 for reverse. N is the total number of steps in the forward direction: M is the current step (0 to 3) as in the table. The loop has extra input for controlling direction. P is used to vary the delay period in line 220. Each time round the loop the current position is found by using the modulo command. As N increases, this produces the values 0, 1, 2, 3, 0, 1,... If N goes negative, as it will if the motor is run mainly in reverse, the modulo is negative 0, -3, -2, -1, 0, ... It is given a suitable positive value by adding 4 to it, causing the program to step through array F() in the reverse order. Line 200 outputs the stored value to the motor. In line 210, N is incremented or decremented as required. After the delay of line 220 the loop repeats.

With the program as printed, the motor runs at about 3.3 revolutions per minute. To increase the speed, increase P to 20 and delete the *1000 from line 220. The speed is then about 500 rpm. The *1000 may be changed to other values to give different ranges of speed. This program can be adapted by cutting out the control statements that are not needed in a particular application. Note that N=0 when the robot arm (or other mechanical part) is in its starting position. Given the current value of N, its present position can be calculated at any instant. This feature can be used, for example, to turn the motor for a specified number of steps. The program runs until N reaches a given value. If a program contains a line such as '215 IF N=24 THEN STOP', the number of 7.5° steps is 24, which produces a half-turn rotation of exactly 180°. In this way we can control the amount of rotation of a robot arm very precisely.

Voltage Conversions

In some applications it is necessary to convert an analogue voltage to digital form to be read by the computer, or for the computer to produce a digital output which is converted to a voltage. The conventional ADC of Figure 6.10 can provide input to a computer. The outputs D_0 to D_7 are fed to the two input registers 03BE and 03BD. They are read by and then turned into a numerical value by using the command on p. 160:

```
OUT &H03BE,&H04
A = INP(&H03BE)
C = INP(&H03BD)
F = A + (C AND 240) XOR 139
```

F takes a value ranging from 0 to 255. This is then processed to calculate voltages, temperatures, positions and other variable quantities which may then be used in decision-taking lines such as 'IF F > 128 THEN ...'. A simpler method of conversion, employing the 507C, is described in Chapter 11 for use in conjunction with the BASIC Stamp, but it is equally suitable for use with a PC. Some other interfaces in Chapter 11 are well-suited to the PC besides.

Conversely, though less often, a digital output may be converted to a voltage using a DAC as in Figure 6.11. The varying voltage, perhaps after having been amplified by an operational amplifier (Figs 6.2 – 6.4), may be used to drive a motor, a lamp, a voltage-controlled oscillator.

Chapter 11

CONTROL BY MICROCONTROLLER

A desk-top computer such as a PC is appropriate for controlling a static and physically large system such as a lathe or a model railway but is less suitable for mobile and portable systems, such as a robot vehicle or a mobile telephone. Also, the control functions are so simple that it is a waste of the resources of a PC to put it in control. Many items of equipment from washing machines to computer printers are adequately controlled by a microcontroller. This is essentially a computer reduced to its essentials. It comprises a microprocessor, control unit and memory (usually very little), often all fabricated on the same chip. There is no full-scale keyboard, no monitor, and there are no disc drives. There are many such microcontrollers available but for this chapter we have chosen the BASIC Stamp. This is a microcontroller system assembled on a PCB measuring only 35mm × 10mm (the BS1 version). When quiescent, it takes only 20µA, so that it can run for days or even weeks on a 9V PP3 battery. It can also be powered from a 5V regulator, or from an external non-regulated source between 6V and 15V. This makes it ideal for hand-held battery-powered projects.

Another advantage of the Stamp is that it is programmable in BASIC. The version of BASIC includes most of the standard BASIC commands and also some special ones related to its use as a microcontroller. There is room in its 256 byte ROM for about 80 program lines, which is more than enough for most control applications. The ROM is a electrically erasable programmable ROM (EEPROM). Once the Stamp has been programmed (this is done on the PC, then downloaded) it retains the program indefinitely when power is turned off. There are also 16 bytes of RAM for data storage. The Stamp is accompanied by a Handbook, a disc with the programming software and many sample programs, a connector to the printer port of the PC, and a carrier board on which there is a prototyping area. Additional Stamps are available at a reasonably low price.

The Handbook contains full instructions for programming and using the Stamp, as well as application notes and programs.

These include several often-required control applications such as controlling and testing servos, a stepper-motor controller, interfacing an ADC, measuring input pulses, reading temperature from a thermistor, using a 16-key keypad, and obtaining analogue output. Some of these make use of a LCD display unit driven by the Stamp. Because these projects are described in the handbook, we shall concentrate in this chapter on simpler BASIC programs, to introduce the reader to the Stamp's special BASIC commands. This will help the reader to get started with the Stamp and to adapt some of the programs in Chapter 10 to run on the Stamp.

One-Bit Output and Input
Making a single output go high or low and reading from a single output are the fundamental operations required for all control systems. The aim of the following project is the same as that of Project 24.

Project 27 – One-Bit Output

The first step is to provide connections between the Stamp and the outside world. You will probably prefer to set up this project on a breadboard instead of the prototyping area. Either wire up a 14-pin single-in-line socket to fit on the 14-pin plug of the carrier board, or solder wires directly into the row of holes that runs beside the 14-pin plug. Figure 11.1 shows the required connections. The output pins can provide up to 20mA each, which is enough to drive an LED directly. They can also sink up to 25mA as inputs, but no more than 40mA should be sourced or 50mA sunk at the same time. A program to flash the LED is:

```
'Flasher 1
DIRS=%11111111
FOR B0=1 to 10
TOGGLE 0
PAUSE 1000
NEXT
```

This flashes the LED 5 times. A major difference between the listing of this program and one written in GWBASIC is that

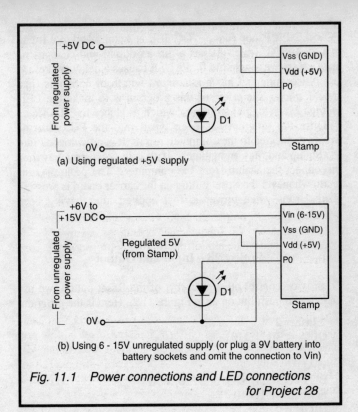

(a) Using regulated +5V supply

(b) Using 6 - 15V unregulated supply (or plug a 9V battery into
battery sockets and omit the connection to Vin)

*Fig. 11.1   Power connections and LED connections
for Project 28*

there are no line numbers. The program may be typed in lower
case, if preferred. For listings in this book we use upper-case
so that key-words can more easily be identified in the des-
criptive text. REM statements can begin with REM, as in
GWBASIC, or be preceded by a '. There are only 8 input/out-
put pins and their direction is usually specified at the beginning
of a program, or later if they are to be changed. Some commands automatically change the direction before executing. In
this listing all the pins are specified as outputs by making the
directions command DIRS equal to the binary number
11111111, the preceding % indicating that this is in binary
format. B0 is one of the 14 bytes set aside in RAM for storage

of data; here it is being used for storing the counter of the FOR ... NEXT loop runs. TOGGLE is a command, not found in GWBASIC, which makes a pin an output and changes its state. Here we toggle pin 0. PAUSE causes a delay, expressed in milliseconds and has a maximum length of 65535ms (just over 1 min). The effect of this program is to make the LED *change state* (toggle) ten times, which produces five flashes.

Once the program has been typed into the PC, with the Stamp connected to the computer, run it. It is downloaded into the Stamp and runs immediately. If all is in order, you may then disconnect the Stamp from the computer. The program runs again whenever the Reset button on the carrier board is pressed. It also runs when power is first applied after having been switched off.

Project 28 – Input and Output

To provide control other than that of the Reset button, we use an external push-button as in Figure 11.2. Here is the program:

```
'Flasher 2
DIRS = %11111101
B2=0
WAIT:
BUTTON 1, 0, 255, 0, B2, 0, WAIT
FOR B0=1 TO 10
HIGH 0
PAUSE 1000
LOW 0
PAUSE 1000
NEXT
```

In this program the zero in the DIRS command makes pin 1 an input. The next line clears the byte B2 ready for use in connection with the BUTTON command. Before we get to this there is the WAIT: statement. The BASIC has no line numbers but uses *labels* instead. WAIT is an *address label*, a label marking a point in the program to which the microcontroller will jump. The label may be any word we choose (except a keyword or variable), and is defined the first time it is used by

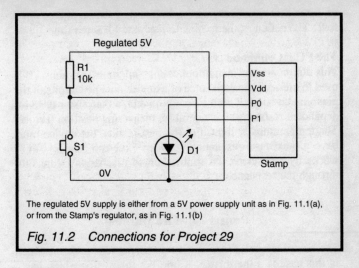

The regulated 5V supply is either from a 5V power supply unit as in Fig. 11.1(a),
or from the Stamp's regulator, as in Fig. 11.1(b)

Fig. 11.2   Connections for Project 29

placing a colon after it.

The BUTTON command is a complex one that is applicable
to any input, whether it comes from a push-button, a
microswitch or a logic input. The 7 parameters in the program
above mean:

The *pin* to read is pin 1
The *downstate*, which is 0, specifies that the input is 0 when
    the button is *pressed*
The *delay*, when set to 255, debounces the button and
    there is no auto-repeat
The *auto-repeat rate* is zero (because there is no auto-repeat)
The *byte-variable* is B2, already cleared for use as the
    button's workspace
The *target state* is 0; the program is to branch when the
    button *not* pressed
The *address* to branch to is WAIT

The effect of BUTTON with the parameter as given above is
to make the program monitor pin 1, branching back to WAIT
repeatedly until the button is pressed. Then the program runs on
to a LED-flashing loop. Here we use HIGH and LOW instead

of TOGGLE. HIGH 0 makes pin 0 high; LOW 0 makes pin 0 low. The action of the loop is to flash the LED ten times.

The POT Command

This command has many applications in control systems. It is used to measure the resistance of a device attached to one of the pins. It can be used with a potentiometer, a thermistor or light-dependent resistor so it is useful for measuring position (Project 31), temperature or light. For the best results, the device must have a maximum resistance between 5kΩ and 50kΩ. POT works by measuring the time taken to discharge a capacitor through the resistance.

Project 29 – Fire Warning

The circuit (Fig.11.3) shows how to connect the resistor, which in this case is a thermistor. Choose a thermistor which has a resistance of about 50kΩ at room temperature. The program is:

```
'Fire warning 1
DIRS = %11111110
LOOP:
POT 0,75,B0
IF B0>100 THEN LOOP
HIGH 1
PAUSE 400
LOW 1
PAUSE 400
GOTO LOOP
```

Pin 0 is set as an input and the other pins as outputs. POT measures the value of a resistance connected to pin 0, scales it down by multiplying by 75/256, and then stores the result as byte B0. Then comes an IF ... THEN decision. If B0 is more than 100, it is considered that the temperature is not danger-ously hot. In this case the program loops back to LOOP. This process repeats indefinitely until B0 falls below 100. Then the program drops through to the last 5 lines, which flash the LED and return to LOOP. As long as the temperature is

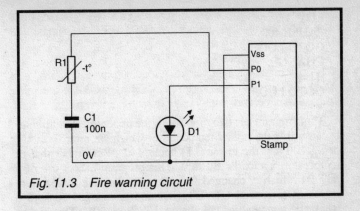

Fig. 11.3   Fire warning circuit

unduly high the loop includes the flash routine. The LED flashes to warn of the high temperature. This continues until the temperature falls below the triggering level.

When running this program you may need to alter the scale value (75 as shown) and also the limit value, presently 100. The exact values required depend on the characteristics of the thermistor and the exact value of the capacitor. The output activity need not be restricted to flashing an LED. It could ring a bell or sound a siren, flash mains-powered lamps or perform even more complicated actions.

As generally happens, there are difficulties if the temperature hovers around the triggering point. The warning operates intermittently. The way to avoid this is to introduce hysteresis, in other words, to give the program a kind of Schmitt trigger action (p. 90):

```
'Fire warning 2
DIRS = %11111110
b1=0
LOOP:
POT 0,75,B0
IF B0>100 and B1=0 THEN LOOP
B1=1
IF B0>140 AND B1=1 THEN CHANGE
HIGH 1
PAUSE 400
```

```
LOW 1
PAUSE 400
GOTO LOOP
CHANGE:
B1=0
GOTO LOOP
```

This program has two *thresholds*, the upper threshold (*upper* because it is the higher temperature) which we refer to as UT being 100 and the lower (LT) being 140. Remember that as temperature increases B0 falls. This program makes use of a *flag* B1 which is changed from 0 to 1 when the temperature increases to exceed UT (B0<100) and is changed back to 0 when the temperature falls below LT (B0>140). This means that the LED begins to flash when the temperature rises *above* UT. But, if the temperature drops, flashing continues until it has dropped *below* LT. The IF ... THEN command can take only an address label in this version of BASIC. We can not say 'IF B0>140 AND B1=1 THEN B1=0. Instead we have to branch to an address label CHANGE, then change B1 and branch back to LOOP.

Controlling Motors
This is an important application for the Stamp, particularly for use in model vehicles and small robots.

Project 30 – Motor Speed Control

This is a general-purpose project that can be simplified or modified to suit the situation. The Stamp is controlled by three push-buttons: ON/OFF, Increase speed, and Decrease speed (Fig.11.4). The program is similar in action to that listed on p. 162. As the program cycles around the main loop, a constant value related to pulse width is incremented or decremented and the Stamp produces a series of high pulses of variable width. In this program the low period is constant in length. This is because the Stamp's BASIC runs slower than GWBASIC. The time taken to interrogate the buttons is relatively long and does not need to be extended. The listing is:

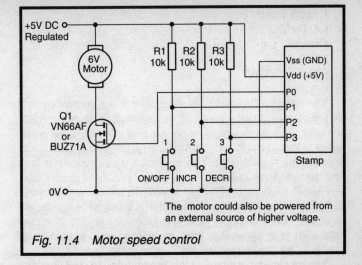

Fig. 11.4   Motor speed control

```
'Motor 1
INITIAL:
B0=0
B1=0
B2=0
B3=125
LOW 0
WAIT:
BUTTON 1, 0, 255, 0, B0, 0, WAIT
LOOP:
BUTTON 2, 0, 255, 0, B1, 1, INCR
TAP1:
BUTTON 3, 0, 255, 0, B2, 1, DECR
TAP2:
BUTTON 1, 0, 255, 0, B0, 1, CEASE
PULSOUT 0, B3
GOTO LOOP
INCR:
B3=B3+5  MAX 1000
GOTO TAP1
DECR:
```

177

```
B3=B3-5 MIN 60
GOTO TAP2
CEASE:
LOW 0
GOTO INITIAL
```

The program first clears the bytes which are the workspaces of the buttons. Then it puts 125 in B3 which is the pulse width variable. It is important to begin with a value above the minimum to kick the motor into rotating. The program then waits in a loop until the ON/OFF button (Button 1) is pressed. It then interrogates buttons 2 and 3 and, if either of these are pressed, it goes to routines at INCR or DECR to increase or decrease B3. There are two useful command MAX and MIN which prevent the value exceeding or falling below set levels. You may find with your motor that you can reduce the minimum pulse width by programming the MIN value lower than 60.

The operative command in this program is PULSOUT which delivers from pin 0 a high pulse of length dependent on B3. The pulse length is $B3 \times 10\mu s$. Speed is increased or decreased by pressing the buttons repeatedly, not by pressing and holding them, as they are programmed for no auto-repeat. Pressing the ON/OFF button is detected at the second BUTTON 0 command, sending the computer to CEASE which makes pin 0 low and sends the computer back to the beginning of the program.

Project 31 – Servomotor Control

This program uses two rotary potentiometers to sense position (Fig.11.5). One (VR1) is driven by reduction gears from the motor, the other (VR2) is rotated manually (or possibly by other means) to set the position to which the servo must turn. For best results these should be precision servo potentiometers, but cermet potentiometers are adequate for many applications. The other input to the Stamp is a pushbutton for ON/OFF control. Two output pins are used, one to switch on the motor, the other to control the reversing relay.

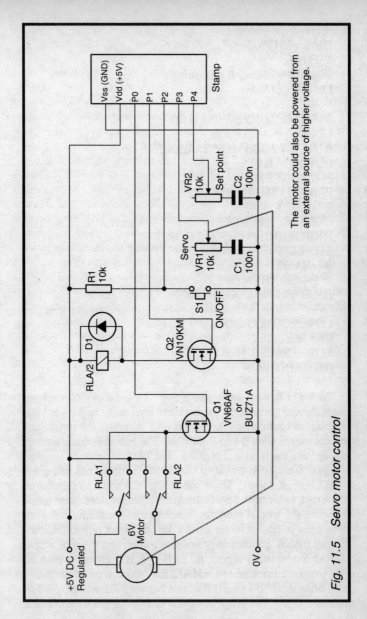

The motor could also be powered from an external source of higher voltage.

Fig. 11.5 Servo motor control

179

```
'Servomotor control
DIRS=%11100011
INITIAL:
B0=5:B1=0:B2=0:B3=0:B4=0
LOW 0:LOW 1
WAIT:
BUTTON 2,0,255,0,b1,0,WAIT
LOOP:
BUTTON 2,0,255,0,b1,1,CEASE
POT 3,124,B2
POT 4,133,B3
IF B2<B3 THEN SMALLER
B4=B2-B3
IF B4<B0 THEN OFF
HIGH 0:HIGH 1:GOTO LOOP
SMALLER:
B4=B3-B2
IF B4<B0 THEN OFF
HIGH 0:LOW 1:GOTO LOOP
OFF:
LOW 0:GOTO LOOP
CEASE:
LOW 0:PAUSE 1000
GOTO INITIAL
```

To avoid this program stretching to several pages, we have
placed some commands on the same line, separated by colons.
The initial routine sets the values of 5 variables B0 to B4, and
makes output pins 0 and 1 go low. The program then waits in
a loop until the button is pressed. The POT commands measure
the resistances connected to pin 3 (VR1, the servo) and pin 4
(VR2, the set point). The scale values 124 and 133 depend on
the exact value of the potentiometers; these values were found
by using the special program included with the Stamp software.
You need to find suitable values for your own potentiometers.
Stamp BASIC handles only positive integers so the next step is
to find out which is bigger, B2 or B3. If B2 is smaller than B3
the program branches to SMALLER. Otherwise it continues
and finds out if B4 (the difference between B2 and B3) is less
than B0 (=5). The purpose of this is to establish a *dead band*.

When the circuit is operating the motor turns in a direction so as to reduce B4. As this reaches zero, the mechanism may overshoot, in which case the motor must reverse and approach the set point from the opposite direction. This produces a hunting action in which the mechanism is continually reversing to and fro about the set point. The dead band ensures that the motor is turned off when B4 becomes reasonably close to zero. The width of the dead band can be set by altering the value assigned to B0 at the beginning of the program.

If B4 is not less than B0 the program proceeds to turn on the motor and energise the relay before returning to repeat the loop again. The same operation is performed if B2 is smaller than B3, except that the relay is de-energised to reverse the direction of motion. If B4 is less than B0, the OFF routine turns off the motor, and returns to the main loop, which the computer cycles, waiting for B4 to exceed B0, in which event the motor starts running again in the appropriate direction. If during the main loop the computer detects that the button has been pressed, it branches to the CEASE routine, turns off the motor and returns to the beginning of the program.

When setting up this program you may need to invert the switching of the relay, depending on the direction the motor turns in. If the mechanism does not home on to the set point but deviates more and more widely from it, exchange the HIGH 1 and LOW 1 commands in the main loop.

It is possible to combine this program with the pulse-generating action of the previous program. If pulse width is made proportional to the size of B4, the servo moves rapidly when the mechanism is far from the set point, and slows down as it approaches the set point. This is *proportional control*. As an alternative to VR2 for determining the set point, it is possible to use an array of four photodiodes to detect the position of a mask marked according to the Gray code (Fig.7.5). The 4-bit input is read as 0, 1, 3, 2, 6, ..., 8 from positions 0 to 15. This sequence is most easily decoded by using the LOOKDOWN command. If the input from the photodiodes is stored in B3 and the decoded position is to be stored back in B3, for example, the command is:

LOOKDOWN B3, (0,1,3,2,6,7,5,4,12,13,15,14,10,11,9,8), B3

B3 then holds the actual linear position and the servo motor can be switched so as to bring it to the set point. For a way of inputting the set point, see the program on p. 177.

Display and 'Keyboard' Programs

One of the chief though inevitable limitations of the Stamp is that it has only 8 pins to act as inputs or outputs. This is the price paid for its small size and low cost, and is no disadvantage in many applications. The handbook shows how to interface a 16-key keypad and an LCD alphanumeric display so there is no real problem in communicating with the Stamp. Here we describe some programs for simpler, inexpensive input and display devices.

Project 32 – One-Digit Numeric Display

This is useful when running counting programs, assuming that the maximum count required is 9. The display consists of a 7-segment LED display connected as in Figure 11.6. Note that the display must be of the *common cathode* type. A demonstration program is:

```
'Counter
DIRS = %01111111
LOOP:
LOOKUP B0, (63, 6, 9, 1, 79, 102, 109, 125, 7, 127, 111),
B1
PINS = B1
PAUSE 1000
B0=B0+1
IF B0=10 THEN ZERO
GOTO LOOP
ZERO:
B0=0: GOTO LOOP
```

The program requires 7 pins as outputs. It depends on the use of a *lookup table*, telling the Stamp which pins to make high to produce the numerals. Given that there are seven segments, we need a table of 7-bit binary numbers in which a

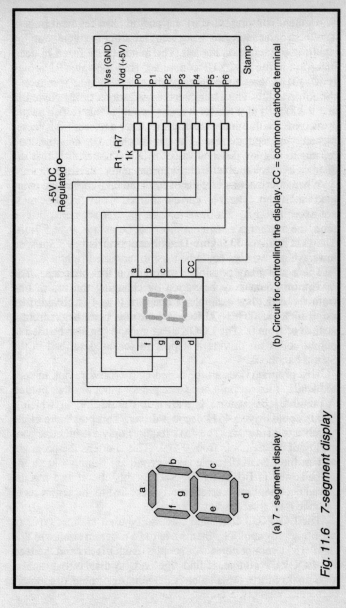

Fig. 11.6 7-segment display

(a) 7 - segment display

(b) Circuit for controlling the display. CC = common cathode terminal

lit segment is represented by a 1 and an unlit segment by a 0. The bits representing each segment are from segment a on the right to segment g on the left. The numbers are listed in decimal form in the LOOKUP command. Thus the value 91, which is 1011011 causes segments a, b, d, e, g to light up, producing the numeral '2'. The numeral to be produced is held in byte B0, and the looked up code for it is put into B1. This is then output to the pins to illuminate the display. After a pause, B0 is incremented, reduced to zero if it has reached 10, and the loop repeats to display the new value of B0. The result is that the display cycles repeatedly through the numerals from 0 to 9.

When constructing circuits of this kind take care not to overload the Stamp. The total current sourced at any one time must not exceed 40mA. As there may be up to 7 segments lit at a time, the current per segment must not be greater than 5.7mA. The 1kΩ resistors in Figure 11.6 limit the current to 3.3mA, so lower-value resistors could be used to increase brightness.

There are many possible variations on this program. The maximum count may be varied by changing the fourth line from the end. For example, a count of 0 to 4 is obtained by using IF B0=5 THEN ZERO. Or the count can begin from 1 instead of from 0. The LOOKUP command can also be used to output codes for driving a stepper motor, as described in the Stamp handbook.

This program does all the decoding by software but, in consequence, it leaves only one spare pin for input or other output. A possible compromise is shown in Figure 7.9, in which a Stamp could drive a 4511 decoder/driver. This puts more of the action into hardware. The 4511 requires only a 4-bit code consisting of the numbers from 0 to 9. This shortens the program, so that the LOOKUP table is not required. Simply output the value stored in B0, using PINS=B0. This circuit also has the advantage that more current can be supplied to the segments to provide a brighter display.

The LOOKUP command can also be used in other types of counting program. The Stamp can run a program similar to that on p. 155 to count objects or people. Each time round the loop the LOOKUP command finds the code to display the present value held in B0. This value is the number of objects counted.

Counting is reset to zero by pressing the reset button on the Stamp carrier board.

Project 33 – A One-Key Keyboard

The counter program is the basis of a simple input procedure. The LED display cycles through a sequence of numbers, as above. Each number corresponds to a different task that the Stamp is to perform, or to a different value (such as a set point) that is to be registered. There is one key, which the user presses when the appropriate task number is displayed, causing the Stamp to perform the selected task. The circuit is the same as in Figure 11.6 or 7.9 with the addition of a push-button wired as S1 in Figure 11.5 but connected to pin 7. The main program loop is essentially the same as in Project 32 with an additional line after the PAUSE 1000:

IF PIN7=0 THEN TASKS

Here we use another way of getting input when it is to result in a branch to a routine. The label TASKS follows the end of the existing program and sends the Stamp to one of a number of tasks, depending on the current value in B0:

TASKS:
BRANCH B0,(up, down, left, right)

The labels in brackets are the routines for performing different actions. In this example the counter runs from 0 to 3 and the mechanism (for example a robot arm) is moved up, down, left or right according to whether the button is pressed on 0, 1, 2, or 3. It might be preferred to have the numbers run from 1 to 4. In this case B0 is given the value 1 initially, the fourth line up becomes IF B0=5 THEN UNITY, and the ZERO routine becomes:

UNITY:
B0=1: GOTO LOOP

The BRANCH command needs to be modified because the bracketed list begins with an item corresponding to B0=0. Insert a dummy item at the beginning of the list:

It is easy to modify the codes of the LOOKUP table to display alphabetic characters such as 'u, d, l, r' instead of numerals.

Measuring Pulse Length

The Stamp handbook describes several applications for using PULSIN, which measures pulse length. The tachometer routines are of special interest in control systems. Another useful technique is to use a 4046 voltage-controlled oscillator to compensate for the logarithmic response of certain sensors and produce a linear response ADC. An ADC that provides a direct and linear input to the Stamp (or to a PC) is the 507C voltage-to-time converter (Fig.5.6). The pulse length is directly proportional to the input voltage and all that is necessary is to use the PULSIN command to measure the pulse length. The value obtained can be compared with a set point value or in other ways used to initiate suitable action. This is a far simpler ADC technique than using a conventional converter such as the ZN427E (Fig.6.10), which takes up all eight of the Stamp's pins as inputs.

Chapter 12

SEQUENTIAL CONTROL

When a system performs a number of different actions one after another, we call it *sequential control*. Some or perhaps all of the actions may involve loop control, either open or closed. When the sequence of actions is complete, the system may either stop or repeat the sequence a few times or indefinitely. In general, sequential control systems can be divided into two types, *time-based* or *event-based*. In a time-based system, an action is begun at a given point in time, irrespective of what else is happening in the system. A system for turning street lamps on or off according the time of day is a time-based system. Such a system need re-timing as the seasons progress. By contrast, an event-based system performs its actions when certain events occur. A system for controlling street lamps by the level of daylight is an example of an event-based system. The event that triggers the turning on of lamps is the falling of light level below a set point for a significant period. The lamps come on earlier on a dull day, and there is no need to adjust the settings according to season.

Although analogue sensors may be required in some systems, a sequential system relies mainly on logic ics, with which we include timer ics. Such being the case, it is often more convenient to implement sequential control with a computer or microcontroller program. In this chapter we look at logic hardware for building sequential systems and also describe equivalent software solutions.

Time-Based Systems

One of the simplest forms of time-based system is based on a *Johnson counter*. This is a standard binary counter with the addition of a decoding circuit so that at any given time only one of its outputs is high. The output that is high triggers a relevant part of the system into action. Figure 12.1 shows a typical circuit of a five-stage counter. The basic timing period is provided by the 7555 timer ic (IC1, Fig.12.1), wired in astable mode, so that it produces a series of square pulses. Its period is

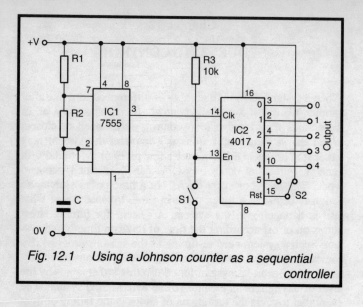

Fig. 12.1   Using a Johnson counter as a sequential controller

determined by the values of R1, R2 and C, where the frequency, $f = 1.44/(R1 + 2 \times R2)C$. Remembering that electrolytic capacitors have appreciable leakage, which limits the largest capacitance that can be used, the maximum period obtainable with a 7555 is only a few minutes. IC2 is enabled by closing switch S1. It is reset by a high input to pin 15, by switching S2. After it is reset, switch S2 so as to connect pins 1 and 15. Output 0 is high and other outputs are low. The counter in IC2 is triggered each time the output of IC1 goes high. Then output 0 of IC2 goes low and output 1 goes high. At successive counts outputs 2, 3, 4, and 5 go high in turn but, as soon as output 5 goes high, this instantly resets the counter to 0. The result is a high output from 0, 1, 2, 3, 4 in turn, repeating until S1 is opened. Only six outputs are used in Figure 12.1. Further outputs are available from pins 5 (output 6), 6 (output 7), 9 (output 8) and 11 (output 9). Any output can be used to reset the counter, to produce cycles of different numbers of stages. If all 10 outputs are to be used, the counter automatically resets at the end of each cycle and the reset input needs to be switched to 0V while counting is in process. An alternative to

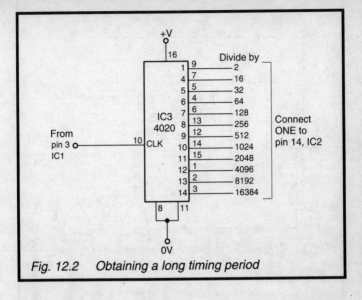

Fig. 12.2   Obtaining a long timing period

the 4017 is the 4022, which has eight stages and has different output pins.

If the frequency of the timer is too high, one solution is to use a long-period timer such as the 2240 (Fig.8.9). This ic has a counter/divider inside it to reduce the frequency by a half at each counting stage. The same result can be obtained by using a counter/divider to reduce the frequency from a 7555, as in Figure 12.2. The complete circuit is that of Figure 12.1 but with IC3 connected between pin 3 of IC1 and pin 14 of IC2. Since the 4020 is a 14-stage counter it reduces the frequency by a maximum of 1/16384. If the period of IC1 is 1 minute, the period of the 14th output of IC3 is 16384 minutes, or over 11days. The only divisions not available from this divider are 1/4 and 1/8. Another use for the divider is to give greater precision. Provided that excessively long periods are not required, the capacitor used with IC1 can be a low-value but high-precision high-stability type, such as a silvered mica capacitor.

Once an output of the Johnson counter has gone high, there are several ways in which it can exert control. Some of these are shown in Figure 12.3. Very often the control will be direct,

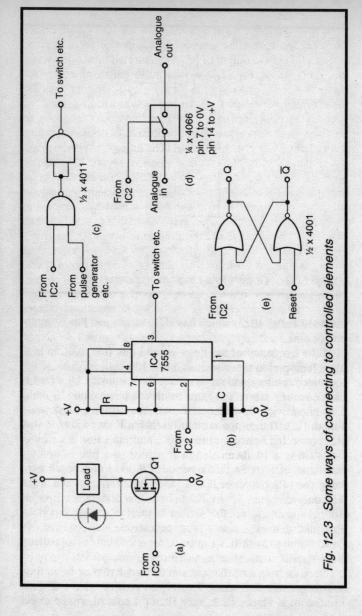

Fig. 12.3 Some ways of connecting to controlled elements

190

through a transistor switch of suitable wattage, as in Figure 12.3a. If the controlled element is to operate for a specific period of time, the output of IC2 is connected to a timer, wired as a monostable (Fig.12.3b). The pulse length of the monostable is $p = 1.1 \times RC$. This period may be shorter than the basic timing period of IC1 (for example, to flash a lamp, or sound a warning siren). Or it may be longer (for example, to turn on a heater), provided that it will have switched off before the output of IC2 goes high again. The timer is triggered when the output goes low at the *end* of a period. Figure 12.3c shows how the output can be used to enable a train of pulses, for example, to turn on a motor controlled by a switch-mode circuit (p. 3). In the circuit shown, the pulse train when enabled is inverted by the first gate. This may be suitable to use, in which case the second gate is not required to re-invert it. The transmission gate of Figure 12.3d serves as a switch to turn an analogue signal on or off. This may be used to turn a sound signal on. If there are several transmission gates with their outputs all connected to the input of an ADC, they may be turned on one at a time at different stages in the cycle to allow voltages from several different sensors to be read in turn. Figure 12.3e shows a set-reset circuit composed of NOR gates. This is triggered by a high pulse; its Q output changing from high to low. The $\overline{Q}$ output changes from low to high. The circuit stays in this state until reset by a high pulse to the reset input. This circuit can be used to trigger an action which continues until it is complete. For example, in a curtain control system, it could trigger a motor to run until the curtain reaches a limit switch, which produces a high pulse to reset the circuit and stop the motor. The set-reset circuit can also be triggered by a pair of outputs from the counter. In this way it is, for example, possible to energise a relay at the beginning of count 2 and release it at the beginning of count 7. Another possible use for the output of IC2 is to enable a series of 3-state devices (Fig.10.11) to place their digital signals on a common bus in sequence.

The counter increments at equal time intervals so all actions are triggered at equal intervals of time. Sometimes it may be useful to be able to make an action run for two or more time intervals. This can be done by using a monostable, as in Figure 12.3b or a set-reset circuit, as in Figure 12.3e. Another method

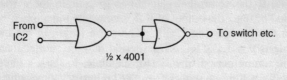

Fig. 12.4   Producing a high output for 2 periods

is to OR two outputs of the counter so that a high output is produced for two periods. The periods need not be consecutive
ones. Figure 12.4 shows the logic, with a second NOR gate as
an inverter to produce the high when both inputs are high (one
could of course use a plain OR gate but somehow it's generally easier to use two NOR gates. Longer or more periods may
be ORed by using a 4025 (for 3), a 4002 (for 4) or a 4078 (for
8). Unused inputs must be wired to used ones if not all inputs
are required.

Another way of producing time intervals of different lengths
is to use cascaded timers wired as monostables (Fig.12.5).
Timer 1 is triggered and produces a high output of the required
length, which perhaps switches on a transistor controlling a
motor. At the end of the period the output goes low, so triggering timer 2, which may control a solenoid. The period of time
2 may be very different from that of timer 1, in fact Timer 1
could run the motor for 5 minutes (a cooling fan) while timer 2
might energise the solenoid for only a millisecond, to release a
catch. This process can be continued for any number of

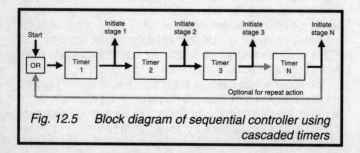

*Fig. 12.5   Block diagram of sequential controller using
cascaded timers*

192

timers, producing a sequential action. The last timer in the chain may complete the sequence or its output may be used to trigger the first timer, to repeat the cycle indefinitely.

Computer-Based Time Sequences

Using a computer or microcontroller makes it much easier to control time-driven sequences. A PC is easily able to substitute for the circuit of Figure 12.1:

```
10  REM ** Counter output **
20  N=0
30  OUT H&03BC,2^N
40  For J=1 to 30000:NEXT
50  N=N+1
60  IF N>6 THEN N=0
70  GOTO 30
```

This is a 6-stage output which consecutively turns on bits 0 to 5 in sequence. Line 40 produces a rather short time interval. For longer periods, use TIME$, which represents the computer's clock. This has the form "HH.MM.SS". We extract the value of the seconds count by using X = VAL(RIGHT$(TIME$,2)). Here is a subroutine that can be called to give a delay of any length between 1 and 59 seconds, to the nearest second. Call the subroutine by using this line:

DELAY = 0: GOSUB 100

Type this line with the required length of delay, and use the appropriate line number for the subroutine. Here is the subroutine:

```
100  REM ** Delay subroutine **
110  OFFSET = 0
120  FINISH = VAL(RIGHT$(TIME$,2)) + DELAY
130  IF FINISH>59 THEN FINISH = FINISH - 60:
         OFFSET = -60
140  NOW = VAL(RIGHT$(TIME$,2))
150  IF NOW=0 THEN OFFSET=0
160  NOW = NOW + OFFSET
170  IF NOW=>FINISH THEN RETURN
180  GOTO 140
```

193

The subroutine returns to the main program at the end of the delay period. The delay variable can be of fixed value or may be calculated in the main program, its value depending on sensor readings or other circumstances. Alternatively, it could be obtained from a lookup table depending on which stage of the sequence has been reached. For delays measured in minutes instead of seconds, use the form X = VAL(MID$(TIME$,4,2)). Delay times are as accurate as the computer clock, which is more than adequate for most applications.

A delay of up to 65s is easily obtainable with the Stamp by using the PAUSE command (p. 170). The delay length is varied by using a command such as PAUSE B0, where the value held in BO depends on the result of a calculation, the input from a sensor, or is obtained using LOOKUP. Longer delays are obtained by using PAUSE two or more times. Short delays produced by PAUSE are accurate to a few milliseconds, but the timebase has an accuracy of ±1% so that long pauses can be several seconds or minutes out. For greater accuracy, a simple external crystal clock can be used, as described in the handbook.

Event-Based Systems

In many event-based sequential systems an action is usually triggered at the completion of the previous action. The scheme is very similar to that of the cascaded timers of Figure 12.5. In a way, the cascaded timers can be considered to be an event-based system. Usually a system relies on sensors to detect when the previous stage is complete. In an automatic washing-machine, for example, pressing the start button activates the solenoid which opens the hot-water tap. This initiates the first stage – filling the tub. A level sensor detects when the water has reached the 'tub full' level. This completes the first stage of the sequence; the tap is closed and the heater is switched on. The water is heated until it reaches the prescribed washing temperature. A circuit including a thermistor or band-gap sensor detects when the temperature reaches the set point. This completes the second stage; the heater is turned off and the temperature-measuring circuit is inactivated. The wash motor is switched on and washing begins. This stage is likely to be controlled by a timer to produce the prescribed length of washing time. Washing proceeds from stage to stage in this manner, each stage ending when a sensor detects that the set point has been reached, or that the set time has elapsed. In the early washing machines the control system was purely mechanical, comprising a number of cams and mechanically-operated switches. Modern washing machines rely almost entirely on digital circuitry, based on a microcontroller. More and more devices requiring sequential control, from fax machines to microwave ovens, are controlled in this manner.

When planning an event-based control system, the decision has to be made whether to design and build logic circuits or to program a microcomputer or microcontroller. For simple systems consisting of no more than three or four stages, a logic circuit built from gates, flip-flops and timers is feasible. Figure 5.10 is an example of a logic circuit for an event-based system and it is clear that, even for this simple action, the circuit is fairly complicated. For more intricate action, a computer or preferably a microcontroller is the obvious choice. This not only makes wiring up the reduced amount of hardware that much easier but also allows the system to be adjusted to achieve best performance merely by altering the software.

Appendix

OPEN LOOP CONTROL SUMMARY

A guide to the basic open-loop control circuits can be found on page 198. Other useful circuits may be found in the Projects.

Regulated 5V Supply

A regulated 5V supply is quickly assembled by wiring a 5V regulator circuit to a ready-made mains adapter unit (Fig.A.1). A unit producing 9V or 12V DC is required, capable of delivering a minimum of 300mA. C1 should be soldered as close as possible to the terminals of IC1. The regulator ic will require a heat sink if it is used to supply large currents for long periods.

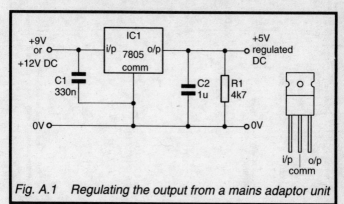

Fig. A.1   Regulating the output from a mains adaptor unit

Other Titles of Interest
BP272 *Interfacing PCs and Compatibles*
BP273 *Practical Electronic Sensors*
BP316 *Practical Electronic Design Data*
BP413 *Practical Remote Control Projects*

Address of Supplier
Milford Instruments, Milford House, 120 High Street, South Milford, Leeds LS25 5AQ. Telephone 01977 683665. Fax 01977 681465. BASIC Stamp, Flexinol wire, Electric Piston.

Power control device	DC lamp, solid-state siren etc. (6V–12V)	AC lamp (230V)	Solenoid, bell, buzzer, valve (12V–24V)	Relay (6V–12V)	DC motor (6V–12V)	AC motor (230V)
Mechanical switch	Page 20	Page 20	As DC lamp	–	As DC lamp	As AC lamp
Variable resistor	Page 20	Commercially built unit	–	–	See switched mode	Commercially built unit
Transistor switch ON/OFF	BJT 2.1, 2.2 MOS 2.3 (all * and †) MOS 2.4, 2.5 (both †)	–	As DC lamp, 3.1, 3.2, 3.3	As DC lamp	As DC lamp 5.3 (direction*†)	As DC lamp + relay
Transistor switch, variable	ON/OFF circuits with variable input (all *)	–	–	–	As DC lamp	–
Thyristor etc.‡ ON/OFF	–	2.6, 2.7, 2.10 (all * and †) 2.10	–	–	–	As AC lamp
Thyristor etc.‡	–	2.8, 2.9, 2.10*†	–	–	–	As AC lamp
Switched mode	–	–	–	–	1.2, 5.5, 5.6*	
Stepper motor	–	–	–	–	5.7†	–
Chapter No.	2	2	3	4	5	5

* suitable for analogue control (may require a Schmitt trigger circuit if used for ON/OFF control)
† suitable for digital control (but some may also be controlled manually or by analogue input, if required)
‡ including triac, opto-coupled thyristor, optocoupled triac